CHRISTMAS

"Do not be afraid;
for see—I am bringing you

GOOD
NEWS

of great joy for all the people:
to you is born this day
in the city of David
a Savior, who is the Messiah,
the Lord."

LUKE 2:10–11

Calligraphy by Melanie Lawson, background illustration by Dan Reed.

CHRISTMAS

An Annual Treasury

VOLUME SIXTY-FIVE

Augsburg

MINNEAPOLIS

IN THIS VOLUME

WHAT WOULD CHRISTMAS BE WITHOUT ANGELS?

IT WAS AN ANGEL who brought the miraculous promise of a baby to an aged priest—a baby who would usher in the long-awaited Messiah. An angel startled young Mary with the astonishing news that she would be the mother of God's Son. Multitudes of brilliant angels heralded God's birth in our world—our flesh—to stunned shepherds on hills outside Bethlehem. The entire story of Christmas is punctuated and ornamented with these messengers of light.

This volume of *Christmas*, too, is ornamented with angels. God's heavenly messengers appear throughout the book. And the message that they long ago carried to the shepherds of Bethlehem is the message that *Christmas* brings to you: "Do not be afraid; for see —I am bringing you good news of great joy for all the people: to you is born this day in the city of David a Savior, who is the Messiah, the Lord."

Here is a preview of some exciting features you'll find inside:

- Three lovely poems beckon you into the Christmas story to hear "The Angels' Anthem," to explore the angels' "Invitation," to feel, today, "The Expectation of Angels."

- In "The Manger Is Empty," a moving account of his young daughter's first experience with death, Walter Wangerin Jr. expresses the deepest, richest meaning of the Christ child's birth.

- Children step back in time to reflect on the shepherds' encounter with angels in "Children, Imagination, and Christmas Angels."

- Art masterpieces of *The Annunciation, The Nativity,* and *The Annunciation to the Shepherds* capture the grandeur of Christmas angels and express the fascination they have inspired in artists throughout the ages.

As you reflect on the Christmas images in words, art, and music, and sample the crafts and recipes in these pages, pause also to reflect on your own feelings about God's heavenly messengers and the astounding news they offer to you. Let their words to the shepherds be the heart of your Christmas celebration this year:

"Do not be afraid . . .

to *you* is born this day . . .

a Savior!"

Wishing you a joyful, fearless Christmas!

—THE EDITORS

TABLE OF CONTENTS

EDITORS: Robert Klausmeier and Ann L. Rehfeldt; ART DIRECTION AND DESIGN: Ellen Maly;
COVER ART DIRECTION: Cindy Cobb-Olson; COVER DESIGN: Cindy Cobb-Olson and Christopher T. Bohnet; COVER
PHOTOGRAPHY: Darrell Eager. With thanks to Ann Potthoff, Elizabeth Boyce, and Pam McClanahan for their assistance.

THE CHRISTMAS STORY

ACCORDING TO

ST. LUKE AND ST. MATTHEW

The angel Gabriel was sent by God to a city of Galilee named Nazareth, to a virgin betrothed to a man whose name was Joseph, of the house of David. The virgin's name was Mary.

And having come in, the angel said to her, "Rejoice, highly favored one, the Lord is with you; blessed are you among women!"

But when she saw him, she was troubled at his saying, and considered what manner of greeting this was.

Then the angel said to her, "Do not be afraid, Mary, for you have found favor with God. And behold, you will conceive in your womb and bring forth a Son, and shall call his name Jesus. He will be great, and will be called the Son of

the Highest; and the Lord God will give him the throne of his father David. And he will reign over the house of Jacob forever, and of his kingdom there will be no end."

Then Mary said to the angel, "How can this be, since I do not know a man?"

And the angel answered and said to her, "The Holy Spirit will come upon you, and the power of the Highest will overshadow you; therefore, also, that Holy One who is to be born will be called the Son of God.

"Now indeed, Elizabeth your relative has also conceived a son in her old age; and this is now the sixth month for her who was called barren. For with God nothing will be impossible."

Then Mary said, "Behold the maiden-servant of the Lord! Let it be to me according to your word." And the angel departed from her.

And it came to pass in those days that a decree went out from Caesar Augustus that all the world should be registered. This census first took place while Quirinius was governing Syria. So all went to be registered, everyone to his own city.

Joseph also went up from Galilee, out of the city of Nazareth, into Judea, to the city of David, which is called Bethlehem, because he was of the house and lineage of David, to be registered with Mary, his betrothed wife, who was with child.

So it was, that while they were there, the days were completed for her to be delivered.

And she brought forth her firstborn son, and wrapped him in swaddling cloths, and laid him in a manger, because there was no room for them in the inn.

Now there were in the same country shepherds living out in the fields, keeping watch over their flock by night. And behold, an angel of the Lord stood

before them, and the glory of the Lord shone around them, and they were greatly afraid.

Then the angel said to them, "Do not be afraid, for behold, I bring you good tidings of great joy which will be to all people. For there is born to you this day in the city of David a Savior, who is Christ the Lord. And this will be the sign to you: You will find a babe wrapped in swaddling cloths, lying in a manger."

And suddenly there was with the angel a multitude of the heavenly host praising God and saying:

"Glory to God in the highest, and on earth peace, good will toward men!"

So it was, when the angels had gone away from them into heaven, that the shepherds said to one another, "Let us now go to Bethlehem and see this thing that has come to pass, which the Lord has made known to us."

And they came with haste and found Mary and Joseph, and the babe lying in a manger. Now when they had seen him, they made widely known the saying which was told them concerning this child.

And all those who heard it marveled at those things which were told them by the shepherds. But Mary kept all these things and pondered them in her heart. Then the shepherds returned, glorifying and praising God for all the things that they had heard and seen, as it was told them.

Now after Jesus was born in Bethlehem of Judea in the days of Herod the king, behold, wise men from the East came to Jerusalem, saying, "Where is he who has been born King of the Jews? For we have seen his star in the East and have come to worship him."

When Herod the king heard these things, he was troubled, and all Jerusalem with him. And when he had gathered all the chief priests and scribes of the people together, he inquired of them where the Christ was to be born.

So they said to him, "In Bethlehem of Judea, for thus it is written by the prophet:

'But you, Bethlehem, in the land of Judah, are not the least among the rulers of Judah; for out of you shall come a Ruler who will shepherd my people Israel.'"

Then Herod, when he had secretly called the wise men, determined from them what time the star appeared. And he sent them to Bethlehem and said, "Go and search diligently for the young child, and when you have found him, bring back word to me, that I may come and worship him also."

When they heard the king, they departed; and behold, the star which they had seen in the East went before them, till it came and stood over where the young child was. When they saw the star, they rejoiced with exceedingly great joy.

And when they had come into the house, they saw the young child with Mary his mother, and fell down and worshiped him. And when they had opened their treasures, they presented gifts to him: gold, frankincense, and myrrh.

Then, being divinely warned in a dream that they should not return to Herod, they departed for their own country another way.

Now when they had departed, behold, an angel of the Lord appeared to Joseph in a dream, saying, "Arise, take the young child and his mother, flee to Egypt, and stay there until I bring you word; for Herod will seek the young child to destroy him."

When he arose, he took the young child and his mother by night and departed for Egypt, and was there until the death of Herod, that it might be fulfilled which was spoken by the Lord through the prophet, saying, "Out of Egypt I called my Son."

But when Herod was dead, behold, an angel of the Lord appeared in a dream to Joseph in Egypt, saying, "Arise, take the young child and his mother, and go to the land of Israel, for those who sought the young child's life are dead."

Then he arose, took the young child and his mother, and came into the land of Israel. ▧

Illustrations by Catherine Rose Crowthers, who lives and works in Oakland, California.

*I*NVITATION

Now there were in the same country shepherds living out in the fields,
keeping watch over their flock by night . . .

Well, it could have been a dream, you know,
or the desert: the moon and the stars—
they play such tricks at night.

Or it could have been the angels singing in the stars,
that glory song—
it could have been a hallelujah-shout from heaven!

Look: it's quiet now,
and it's not so far to Bethlehem.
Let's go and see . . .

SR. MARY WINIFRED, CHS

Sister Mary Winifred, a member of the Community of the Holy Spirit, is the director of St. Cuthbert's and St. Aidan's Retreat
Houses in Brewster, New York. She has written numerous articles and reviews and has co-authored a book on spiritual
growth for women.

Illustration and border by Dan Reed, who lives and works in Providence, Rhode Island.

WAITING FOR JESUS

HAROLD WEBB EPPLEY AND ROCHELLE YOLANDA MELANDER

Outside, the snow-swept prairie grew dark. Lily Carlson stood by the kitchen window, savoring the sounds and smells that filled her house as she watched the sun slip behind the barn. In the living room, Lily's daughter-in-law sang carols as she unpacked ornaments. Lily's son stood awkwardly over the Christmas tree, trying to untangle a string of lights and muttering under his breath.

In the kitchen, three children rushed to finish the Christmas Eve baking. Richard leaned over the table, instructing his younger brother: "First you put on the face and hair; then you frost their wings and clothes; the buttons come last."

Five-year-old Sam nodded, awed by his brother's knowledge. Across the room, Lily's third grandchild peered through the oven window like a cat about to pounce. "And Miss Emily," asked Lily, "what do you think you're doing there?"

"Watching the cookies bake, Gram," replied the girl, not moving her eyes.

"Well, Em, watching won't hurry them along any."

"I know, Gram. But it's more fun than just waiting. Besides, you can see them change while they bake."

Lily smiled, recalling her husband Isaac, who was always watching, always curious. She gazed out the window again, staring at the farm she had called home these past forty years. She watched the barn door shudder in the wind, waited for it to fly open, waited for Isaac to step out into the cold night air and make his way to the house for supper. For a moment, she almost believed it would happen. Then, like a sudden gust of air on a calm winter day, the events of the past year rushed over her. Isaac was dead. It would be a year in April. The barn stood empty.

"Grandma?" asked Sam, stirring Lily from her reverie. "Tell Richard that there are so angels."

Lily took a sip of lukewarm coffee. "Richard," she said with a no-nonsense glare, "I seem to remember a boy who once insisted that his parents take him angel hunting."

"That must have been Sam," mumbled Richard. "I'd never be so naive."

Since his tenth birthday last spring, Richard had made a point of giving up childhood beliefs and quoting words from the dictionary to prove his newfound sophistication.

"No, my dear," Lily insisted softly, "it wasn't Sam. It was you."

"Maybe so, but I was infantile then," said Richard with a grunt. He frowned at his brother who was happily frosting wings on a gingerbread angel.

Lily plopped into a straight-back chair and rested her aching feet for the first time in nearly three hours. Just as she was about to close her eyes, she felt a small body beside her. "Gram? What about tonight? What about waiting for Jesus to come?"

Lily had been expecting that question. "What about it, Sam?"

"Well, I was wondering, Grandpa used to tell us stories and stay with us while we waited for the angels to bring Jesus, but now Grandpa lives with God and he can't be here, and Richard said that Jesus won't come anyway this year." Sam had spoken the entire sentence in one breath, and by the time he was finished, he looked about ready to cry.

Lily grasped him in her arms and squeezed him tight, knowing she needed the hug as much as he did. "Don't worry, Sam. I'm sure Jesus will come this year just like he always has." She tried to speak the words like she really believed them.

Emily paraded the last pan of cookies across the room and set them in line on the table for decorating. "I have an idea," she announced. "Grandma can wait for Jesus with us this year and tell us stories just like Grandpa did."

Sam's eyes grew wide. He threw his arms around Lily's neck and began to jump up and down. "Please, oh please, Gram! Would you? Would you?"

"Okay, okay. I'll give it a try."

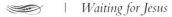

Sam and Emily cheered and raced into the living room to tell their parents. Richard continued his decorating, adding finishing touches to yet another well-groomed gingerbread angel. "Grandma," he said, putting down the knife, "I didn't mean to upset Sam."

He stepped to the doorway and peered into the living room. "It's just that waiting for Jesus was Grandpa's tradition. How can we do it without him?" His voice broke, and all his sophistication suddenly dropped away.

Lily pulled a tissue from her pocket and dabbed at her cheek.

"Oh, Grandma," whimpered Richard. "I'm sorry. You must miss him even more than I do."

Lily nodded.

IN THAT SAME DOORWAY, nearly forty years before, a strapping young farmer had clutched a shoe box to his chest and peered nervously across the room.

"Why, Isaac, is that your Christmas gift for me?" giggled Lily, dancing toward her husband with outstretched arms.

He put the box down and slipped her hands into his own. "If I tell you a story, will you promise not to laugh?"

"I promise." After four months of marriage, he was still learning how to trust her.

"My family has this Christmas tradition," he said, staring at the shoe box.

Lily nodded, recalling her own family's traditions. Every year her mother baked cinnamon rolls. Every Christmas morning, the family would eat them with tea and hot chocolate before opening presents.

"I don't remember when it started," Isaac continued. "I think I'd just turned five. My parents always took us to church, and for weeks all the grownups talked about how Jesus would be coming on Christmas Day."

Lily gazed into her husband's eyes as he told the story which she would come to learn by heart. Mrs. Maki, Isaac's

> *He read aloud the message he had found*
> *beneath the Christmas tree . . .*
> *"For you and for the whole world—your Savior, Jesus."*

Sunday school teacher had told her students that every Christmas God sent Jesus as a gift to the world. And Pastor Larsen, in his booming voice, preached every Sunday in Advent about Jesus' impending arrival. Isaac's father and mother lit candles each evening meal as they prayed, "Come, Lord Jesus, be our guest."

On those nights before Christmas, in the shadows of his bedroom, five-year-old Isaac had peered out the window waiting for Jesus to come. But when Christmas morning arrived and he leaped out of bed to search for the long-awaited guest, he found nothing. He had finally collapsed into his mother's arms, crying tears of bitter disappointment.

"You see," Isaac had explained to his young wife, "I felt like a promise had been broken.

"I don't remember what made things better that year—if they even got better. But the next Christmas we started our tradition. We sat up in my room, my mother and I, and we waited for Jesus together. We lit a candle and she told me stories, and we watched until we both fell asleep.

"And the next morning when I looked under the Christmas tree, I found this." Isaac reached for the shoe box and slipped off the lid. He pulled out a small china baby doll with curly brown hair and shiny blue eyes."

"It's beautiful!" exclaimed Lily.

Isaac reached into the box again, this time pulling out a yellowed piece of paper the size of a postcard. He read aloud the message he had found beneath the Christmas tree twenty years before: "For you and for the whole world—your Savior, Jesus."

"Your mother wrote that?" asked Lily.

"Oh no," replied Isaac with the sincerity of a six-year-old. "Angels did. And they've brought the baby Jesus to the house every Christmas since." He winked and then laughed, unwittingly cradling the doll in his arms.

Lily smiled. She tried to imagine him as a father.

"Are you laughing at me? Don't you like my tradition?" he asked, still the anxious and uncertain groom.

"Isaac, I'm smiling because I love you."

Lily gave birth to a son the next year on a cold, snowy day two weeks before Christmas. In the Christmases that followed, the young family continued Isaac's tradition.

Several years after graduating from college, their only son had come home to live with them on the farm,

starting a business in a nearby town. He brought with him his wife and their baby son, Richard. Isaac had been the one to teach the ritual to their grandchildren.

Now, thought Lily, it is my turn to keep it alive.

AFTER CHRISTMAS EVE SERVICES at church, the children slipped into their pajamas and gathered in the boys' room upstairs. Emily helped her mother carry quilts and blankets from the closet while Sam and Richard pushed their twin beds together near the window. Lily lit two tapered candles and set them in holders on the dresser.

As the children plunged into the beds and covered themselves with blankets, Lily's son arrived from the kitchen with a tray of cookies. "I brought some treats, in case you can't sleep," he joked. After hearing the children's prayers, he headed downstairs to help his wife wrap presents.

The children huddled together facing the window while they chattered and nibbled at Christmas cookies. "Come on," shouted Sam, beckoning to his grandmother and pointing to the spot on the bed he had saved just for her.

Lily was staring at one of the candles, lost in thought. "Grandma!" Sam shouted again, "are you . . ."

Emily cupped a hand over his mouth. "Sshhh!" she whispered. "Grandma's thinking about Grandpa."

The children grew silent. Outside, the wind whistled through the trees and rattled the window.

Lily shook her head and sighed. "I'm sorry, children," she said. "This was always your grandfather's job. I'm not sure what to do."

"We tell stories, Gram. And we watch for angels to bring Jesus," explained Sam. He reached for Lily's arm and pulled her down on the bed beside him.

Richard jumped up and returned with a tattered picture Bible his grandfather had given him years before. He leafed through its pages, stopping at an illustration of Abraham and Sarah entertaining three strange visitors.

"Read that story!" squealed Sam, alternating his attention between the book and his grandmother.

Richard began to read aloud, pausing for dramatic effect at the part where the visitors told old Abraham that his ninety-year-old wife would give birth to a son.

"Gram, Sarah was even older than you when she had her baby, wasn't she?" interrupted Sam.

"That she was," chuckled Lily.

"Grandpa liked that story 'cause the baby's name was Isaac," recalled Emily.

"Yeah," added Richard, "and he'd always tell us that Isaac means laughter, and then he'd laugh really loud." Richard chortled, trying to imitate his grandfather.

Lily smiled, remembering. Sometimes on long, sleepless nights, she would think she still heard Isaac laughing.

"Now it's your turn, Gram," shouted Sam.

"Come on, Gram!" urged Emily, her nose pressed against the window in hopes of spotting an angel.

"Well, I suppose I could tell you about the time I waited for a young man to come home from the army."

"Ooh, Grandma, was he handsome?"

"Oh yes, Emily, and charming as well."

"Disgusting," muttered Richard as he pulled a blanket over his head.

"You're talking about Grandpa, aren't you?"

"Yes, Em." Lily stared across the room at the candles, now only half their original length. "It was Christmas time. We hadn't seen each other for well over a year. He'd been stationed overseas.

"We'd decided that as soon as he returned we'd be married. His train was scheduled to arrive in Fargo at three in the afternoon. Of course, I arrived at the station at quarter past one."

"That sounds like you, Grandma," said Richard, who was lying on his back watching shadows dance across the ceiling. "You're always so . . . so . . . over-punctual."

"Yes, I guess I am," laughed Lily. "But how I longed to see him. I waited for over two hours in the cold, holding my breath every time I thought I heard a train whistle in the distance. Then the station master announced that there was an ice storm in St. Paul and the train would be delayed until seven. I started to cry like a baby."

"Like Sam," teased Richard.

"Sshhh!" whispered Emily. "Tell us more, Gram."

"Well, I was just standing there with tears running down my face when this kind old lady walked up and wrapped her arm around my shoulder. 'I'm waiting, too,' she told me. 'And it's always easier to wait together.' So that's what we did. We told stories and we laughed and we nibbled on sandwiches. Somehow being together made the waiting more bearable, until that train finally arrived."

"And then you got married and lived happily ever after—right, Grandma?"

"Yes, of course, Emily—happily ever after." Lily stood up from the bed and moved the empty cookie plate to the dresser. "And now, children, I think it's time to sleep."

"But Grandma," moaned Emily, "we have to wait for Jesus to come."

From the hallway outside Lily thought she heard the children's parents tiptoeing past toward their bedroom. "I suspect that Jesus may already be here," she said as she kissed Sam on the cheek. "But I'll stay with you, and we can still wait together, even if we are sleeping."

The children decided not to argue. Emily scrambled into one bed and the boys shared the other—just for this Christmas Eve night. They stretched out and pulled the covers up while Lily tucked them in.

Lily blew out the candles and reached for one of the extra blankets brought from the hall closet. She recognized it as the one she'd taken to the hospital for Isaac in the final days. She draped the blanket over her shoulders and stood staring out the window, thinking back to a day in April.

"Lil!"

"Yes, Isaac." She gazed down into his faraway eyes. His arms trembled and his mouth hung open as he gasped for air.

"I'm thirsty."

Lily scooped crushed ice from a cup on the bedstand and slipped it onto her husband's tongue.

"Lil, do you see them?"

"See who, Dear?"

"The angels," he gasped. He was staring over her shoulder.

Lily turned to look. She saw an empty chair beside her own and the sterile white wall of the hospital room.

"Isaac, I don't understand. Are you in pain?"

"The angels are dancing," he continued, as though he hadn't heard her.

She remembered the doctors telling her that in the final stages of cancer he might start to hallucinate.

Isaac kept staring at the wall. "Jesus," he whispered, "I can see Jesus. He's calling to me."

Lily held her breath. Except for the steady ticking of a clock on the bedstand, she heard nothing.

"Such a sight," he exclaimed.

Please, God, Lily prayed, *let me see what he sees.* She began to caress his arm. She kissed his forehead. And then, as quickly as it had come, the epiphany was over. Isaac closed his eyes and fell asleep.

In the hours that followed, Lily never left his side. Together they waited, until death finally parted them.

LILY CLUTCHED THE BLANKET to her chest and shuddered. She turned to where the children lay sleeping and sat down in the chair beside them, drifting off into a deep

sleep. She did not open her eyes until the sun peeked through the window.

"Gram! Gram! It happened!"

Lily woke with a start. Sam was sitting on the bed, leaning over her face and beaming.

"The angels brought Jesus, Gram. Come and see!"

Sam took the steps two at a time as he led Lily down the stairs. In the living room, surrounded by a mountain of presents, Emily sat beneath the tree, cradling the doll in her arms.

"Merry Christmas, Gram!" she smiled, holding the doll up proudly.

Richard sat sprawled out on the sofa, studying the note that had accompanied the doll. "Well, I don't know," he smirked, "this handwriting looks remarkably like . . ."

"Richard!" his father interrupted with a glare. "It's time to eat."

The family gathered around the kitchen table for their traditional Christmas breakfast. "Sam, would you lead us in the blessing?" asked his father.

They folded their hands as Sam began: "Come, Lord Jesus, be our guest and let these gifts to us be blest."

"Amen!" shouted the three children in unison. And, in unison, they reached for the cinnamon rolls. They giggled and chattered as their mother poured hot chocolate into their cups.

Lily leaned back in her chair and smiled. She had yet to see either Jesus or angels. But she knew in her heart that they had come this year—as they had come every Christmas in the past. As they would always come. ◼

Harold Webb Eppley and Rochelle Yolanda Melander are husband and wife, ordained Lutheran pastors, and a free-lance writing team who live in Wauwatosa, Wisconsin. Both grew up in families that treasured Christmas rituals and storytelling. "Waiting for Jesus" was written as a tribute to two children who believe in angels and eagerly await the arrival of Jesus at their home each Christmas.

Illustrations by Shola Friedensohn of Cambridge, Massachusetts, who comes from a family of artists and has a Masters Degree in Sculpture.

THE ANGELS' ANTHEM

GLORY in the birth that lights your way

TO where the Christ has opened heaven's door.

GOD in mercy blessed the world this day

IN giving you his only Son. Adore

THE innocent born here without a stain.

HIGHEST praise to her who bore this child

AND held in faith the sorrow that had lain

ON her, obedient handmaid, undefiled.

EARTH, sing with joy to find your King revealed.

PEACE be to you who ask it in God's name.

GOOD works will flourish and God's grace unsealed

WILL grant salvation, all because he came.

TOWARD you he turns with love, his arms held wide;

MEN, women—all nations—welcomes to his side.

MARY LOU HEALY

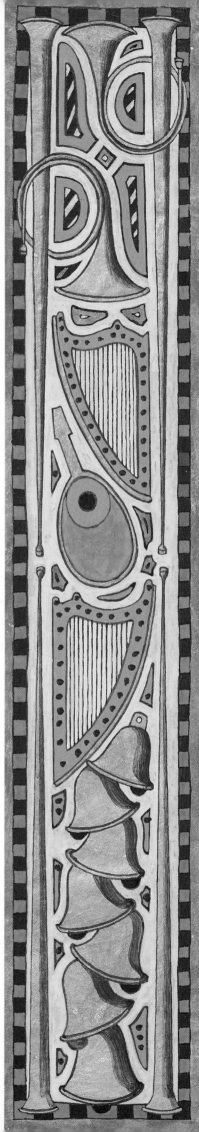

Mary Lou Healy, of Dracut, Massachusetts, likes to write on simple themes: nature, the turning wheel of seasons, faith and the myriad connections that link us to one another. She is deeply moved by the angel stories of the Bible—most of all by the "towering majesty of the multitude of heavenly host praising God at Jesus' birth."

Calligraphy by Melanie Lawson, Arlington Heights, Illinois. Border illustration by Dan Reed.

WORSHIPING WITH ANGELS

Readings, Carols, and Prayers for Christmas

DAVID W. TOHT

Christmas is the season of angels—and for good reason. They appear throughout the biblical Christmas story, encountering, announcing, praising. As God's messengers on earth, they foreshadow the incarnation of Christ. In addition to their marvelous role in the events of Christmas, there is a beauty and mystery about angels that fascinates us.

The following three worship activities are designed to help families, individuals, or small groups prepare for and celebrate Christmas. Each concentrates on angels in a different role, at a different point in the Christmas story. The first two activities could introduce evenings of making or putting up decorations. The third could culminate in group caroling or a sing-along concert of recorded Christmas music.

———— 1 ————

SETTING THE SCENE

Light incense or a scented candle to set the mood for this worship session. Incense traditionally symbolizes the prayers of people rising to God. The subject of our scripture reading, Zechariah, encountered an angel while serving on his rotation as a temple priest. He was in the very act of burning incense during prayers when he had a surprise visit from God's messenger. Zechariah was literally struck dumb by the encounter.

SCRIPTURE READING
LUKE I: 11–19

Then there appeared to him an angel of the Lord, standing at the right side of the altar of incense. When Zechariah saw him, he was terrified; and fear overwhelmed him. But the angel said to him, "Do not be afraid, Zechariah, for your prayer has been heard. Your wife Elizabeth will bear you a son, and you will name him John. You will have joy and gladness, and many will rejoice at his birth, for he will be great in the sight of the Lord. He must never drink wine or strong drink; even before his birth he will be filled with the Holy Spirit. He will turn many of the people of Israel to the Lord their God. With the spirit and power of Elijah he will go before him, to turn the hearts of parents to their children, and the disobedient to the wisdom of the righteous, to make ready a people prepared for the Lord."

Zechariah said to the angel, "How will I know that this is so? For I am an old man, and my wife is getting on in years." The angel replied, "I am Gabriel. I stand in the presence of God, and I have been sent to speak to you and to bring you this good news."

MEDITATION

As popular as angels are today, we often have difficulty visualizing God's messengers actively involved in our world. Part of this difficulty may stem from the images we have of angels.

The Bible says very little about how these creatures look. But it is not likely that they resemble the blond, blue-eyed Dresden dolls pictured in many Christmas card scenes. In scores of instances, the Bible records angelic visitors that apparently had human characteristics. They met people face to face, bearing spoken messages. Abraham invited angels to lunch. They ate and chatted as any human visitors might. Balaam encountered an angel he couldn't see at all—even though his donkey could—but he clearly heard the words of warning the angel spoke. Angels astounded shepherds by filling the night skies with glorious songs of praise. An angel met and consoled the despairing disciples at Jesus' tomb. In each instance, the encounter was on a human plane—with real people in their day-to-day lives—even though its outcome was profoundly life-changing.

The idea of angels entering our world is not a quaint notion; this is one of the most powerful ways in which God has communicated with us. To doubt the reality of angels in our world can limit our understanding of God's activity among us. Angels are an expression of God's love for humanity, a powerful means of meeting us where we are.

HYMN

Oh, Come, Oh, Come, Emmanuel

Oh, Come, Oh, Come, Emmanuel

1 Oh, come, oh, come, Em-man-u-el, And ran-som cap-tive Is-ra-el,
2 Oh, come blest Day-spring, come and cheer Our spir-its by your ad-vent here;

That mourns in lone-ly ex-ile here Un-til the Son of God ap-pear.
Dis-perse the gloom-y clouds of night, And death's dark shad-ows put to flight.

Refrain

Re-joice! Re-joice! Em-man-u-el Shall come to you, O Is-ra-el.

Text: Psalteriolum Cantionum Catholicarum, *Köln, 1710; tr. John M. Neale, 1818–1866, alt. Tune: French processional, 15th cent.*   VENI, EMMANUEL
888888

O most loving Father, you want us to give thanks for all things, to fear nothing except losing you, and to lay all our cares on you, knowing that you care for us. Protect us from faithless fears and worldly anxieties, and grant that no clouds in this mortal life may hide from us the light of your immortal love shown to us in your Son, Jesus Christ our Lord.

——— 2 ———

SETTING THE SCENE

Light a single, small candle, a symbol of the solitary young girl who did not flinch at the grand and troubling news given her by the angel Gabriel.

SCRIPTURE READING

LUKE 1: 26-38

In the sixth month the angel Gabriel was sent by God to a town in Galilee called Nazareth, to a virgin engaged to a man whose name was Joseph, of the house of David. The virgin's name was Mary. And he came to her and said, "Greetings, favored one! The Lord is with you." But she was much perplexed by his words and pondered what sort of greeting this might be. The angel said to her, "Do not be afraid, Mary, for you have found favor with God. And now, you will conceive in your womb and bear a son, and you will name him Jesus. He will be great, and will be called the Son of the Most High, and the Lord God will give to him the throne of his ancestor David. He will reign over the house of Jacob forever, and of his kingdom there will be no end." Mary said to the angel, "How can this be, since I am a virgin?" The angel said to her, "The Holy Spirit will come upon you, and the power of the Most High will overshadow you; therefore the child to be born will be holy, he will be called Son of God. And now, your relative Elizabeth in her old age has also conceived a son; and this is the sixth month for her who was said to be barren. For nothing will be impossible with God." Then Mary said, "Here am I, the servant of the Lord; let it be with me according to your word." Then the angel departed from her.

MEDITATION

It is easy to get the impression that Mary was busy with some everyday task when Gabriel appeared. We almost imagine her dropping a bowl in her surprise. Biblical encounters with angels so often seemed to happen in the midst of mundane, commonplace activities. We find people suddenly shaken out of their routine, jolted into responding to God.

We rightly regard Mary as the very model of obedience to God. Still, she responded to Gabriel in a way all of us can relate to. When told she was a favored one, she didn't seem to react as if this were particularly good news. She was troubled, maybe wishing someone else had been so favored. And she had the presence of mind to ask at least one very practical question. A part of her likely preferred the familiar realm of the everyday—instead of the enormous role she was asked to take.

Still, despite her fear and misgivings, Mary accepted the news as God's will. She chose to walk in the path God set before her. Her response was honest, her obedience full. God asks no more.

HYMN

Lo, How a Rose Is Growing

PRAYER

O God, in your love you have given us gifts which our forebears neither knew nor dreamed of. Mercifully grant that we may not be so occupied with material things that we forget the things which are spiritual and thus, even though we have gained the whole world, lose our souls; through Jesus Christ our Lord.

Lo, How a Rose Is Growing

1 Lo, how a rose is grow - ing, A bloom of fin - est grace; The
2 The rose of which I'm sing - ing, I - sa - iah had fore - told. He
3 The shep - herds heard the sto - ry The an - gels sang that night: How
4 This flow'r, so small and ten - der, With fra - grance fills the air; His

proph - ets had fore - told it: A branch of Jes - se's race Would bear one per - fect
came to us through Mar - y Who shel - tered him from cold. Through God's e - ter - nal
Christ was born of Mar - y; He was the Son of light. To Beth - le - hem they
bright - ness ends the dark - ness That kept the earth in fear. True God and yet true

flow'r Here in the cold of win - ter And dark - est mid - night hour.
will This child to us was giv - en At mid - night calm and still.
ran To find him in the man - ger As an - gel her - alds sang.
man, He came to save his peo - ple From earth's dark night of sin.

© Text: German, 15th cent.; tr. Gracia Grindahl, b. 1943. Tune: Alte Catholische Geistliche Kirchengesang, Köln, 1599.

ES IST EIN ROS
767676

SETTING THE SCENE

This is the perfect time to get out some music and sing carols together, or play some favorite recorded Christmas music, particularly pieces of resounding praise.

SCRIPTURE READING
LUKE 2: 8-20

In that region there were shepherds living in the fields, keeping watch over their flock by night. Then an angel of the Lord stood before them, and the glory of the Lord shone around them, and they were terrified. But the angel said to them, "Do not be afraid; for see—I am bringing you good news of great joy for all the people: to you is born this day in the city of David a Savior, who is the Messiah, the Lord. This will be a sign for you: you will find a child wrapped in bands of cloth and lying in a manger." And suddenly there was with the angel a multitude of the heavenly host, praising God and saying, "Glory to God in the highest heaven, and on earth peace among those whom he favors!"

MEDITATION

Singing together is wonderful. To be enveloped in a joyful noise, sharing as if with one voice lyrics of beauty and meaning, truly takes us out of ourselves.

There is no more beloved image of angels than that of the heavenly host breaking into praise before the dumbstruck shepherds. What was their music like? Was it improvised like joyful, high-flying jazz? Was it richly colored and grand like the chorus of a great oratorio? Was it bold, bright, and spontaneous like great gospel music?

Praise is unabashedly emotional, and that is why music conveys it best. It is a true letting-go in song, forgetting ourselves and allowing the song carry us—mind, body, and spirit—as if on wings.

HYMN

The First Noel

PRAYER

God of majesty, whom saints and angels delight to worship in heaven: Be with your servants who make art and music for your people, that with joy we on earth may glimpse your beauty, and bring us to the fulfillment of that hope of perfection which will be ours as we stand before your unveiled glory. We pray in the name of Jesus Christ our Lord.

David W. Toht is a writer and publisher living in St. Charles, Illinois. He counts participating in the local sing-it-yourself *Messiah* as one of the chief joys of Christmas.

ART CREDITS: Scala/Art Resource, NY. Page 16: S0046702 K65615 Color Transp. Angelico, Fra. *Angel with violin*, S. Marco, Florence, Italy. Page 18: S0019278 K65612 Color Transp. Angelico, Fra. *Music-making angel with lyre*, detail of Linaioli Altarpiece, Museo di San Marco, Florence, Italy. Page 20: S0046708 K65615 Color Transp. Angelico, Fra. *Angel with tambourine*. S. Marco, Florence, Italy.

The First Noel

1 The first No - el the an - gel did say, Was to cer - tain poor
2 They look - ed up and saw ___ a star Shin - ing in the
3 And by the light of that ___ same star Three ___ Wise ___ Men
4 This star drew near to the ___ north - west, O'er ___ Beth - le -

shep - herds in fields as they lay; In fields where ___ they lay, keep - ing their
east ___ be - yond ___ them far; And to the ___ earth it gave ___ great
came ___ from coun - try far; To seek for a king was their ___ in -
hem ___ it took ___ its rest; And there it ___ did both stop ___ and

sheep, On a cold win - ter's night ___ that was ___ so deep.
light, And ___ so it con - tin - ued both day ___ and night.
tent, And to fol - low the star ___ wher - ev - er it went.
stay Right ___ o - ver the place where Je - sus lay.

Refrain

No - el, No -

el, No - el, No - el! Born is the King of Is - ra - el.

5 Then entered in those Wise Men three,   And offered there in his presence
  Full rev'rently upon their knee,   Their gold, and myrrh, and frankincense.

Refrain

Text: English carol, c. 17th cent. Tune: English carol, c. 17th cent.

THE FIRST NOWELL
irregular

THE MANGER IS EMPTY

WALTER WANGERIN JR.

M y daughter cried on Christmas Eve. What should I say to the heart of my daughter? How should I comfort her?

Her name is Mary. She's a child. She wasn't crying the tears of disillusionment, as adults do when they've lost the spirit of the season. No, Mary was longing for Odessa Williams, that old black lady. Mary was longing for her life. That's why she was crying.

WE HAVE A CUSTOM in our congregation: always we gather on the Sunday evening before Christmas, bundled and hatted and happy, and we go, then, out into the sharp December darkness to sing carols. Down the streets of the city we go, the children bounding forward, adults all striding behind, chattering, making congenial noises, puffing ghosts of breath beneath the streetlights, laughing and glad for the company. Does anyone think it will snow? It's cold enough to snow, and the air is still, and the stars are already a snow-dust in heaven.

And so it was that on Sunday evening, the twentieth of December, 1981, we kept our custom and went out caroling. And though we can be silly, and though this is just an ordinary custom, yet we are no ordinary choir. No: many of us sing for "The Sounds of Grace," a choir of legitimate repute. And some of us have been blessed by God with voices the angels would weep to own.

Mary was seven years old then. Dee Dee was eight. Timmy was with us, and the Hildreth children. Most of the children's choir, in fact, had come along. The night was not much different from those that went before— except for this, that when we had finished our round of houses we went to St. Mary's Hospital to sing for several members who were patients at Christmas time. We divided into three groups. As pastor, I myself led a handful of

children to the room of Odessa Williams because her condition was worse than the others.

It was Odessa Williams who made the night different.

The children had never laid eyes on her before. When they crept into the ward and saw her cadaverous body, they were speechless for a while. Scared, I think. Mary's blue eyes grew very large, and I felt pity for her.

Well, I knew what to expect, but Mary didn't. I had been visiting the woman for several years now—first in her apartment, where she'd been housebound, then in the nursing home—and I had watched the wasting of Odessa.

Two years ago she had been a strapping tall woman of strong ways, strong opinions, and very strong affections. Fiercely she had loved the church that she couldn't actually attend. She was particularly fierce regarding her children, the choir, the "Sounds of Grace," though she had never heard them sing. She loved them. She swelled with a grand, maternal love for them.

The disease that kept her housebound and sent her to the nursing home was cancer. Cancer, finally, had laid her in the hospital. And it was cancer that frightened the children when they crept around her bed on Sunday night, coming to sing carols to her.

Mary stood across the bed from me, not looking at me, gazing down at Odessa. Mary's eyes kept growing larger.

So I whispered to all of them, "Sing." But they shuffled instead.

"What's this?" I whispered. "Did you lose your voices? Do you think she won't like it?"

"We think she won't hear," said Mary.

"No, no, sing the same as you always do," I said. "Sing for Miz Williams."

Well, and so they did, that wide-eyed ring of children, though it was a pitiful effort at first. "Away in a Manger," like nursery kids suspicious of their audience. But by the

23

time the cattle were lowing, the children had found comfort in the sound of their own voices and began to relax. Moreover, Odessa had opened her eyes, and there was light in there, and she had begun to pick out their faces, and I saw that Mary was returning Odessa's look with a fleeting little smile. So then they harked it with herald angels, and they found in their bosoms a first noel that other angels did say, and then a marvelous thing began to happen: Odessa Williams was frowning—frowning and nodding, frowning with her eyes squeezed shut, frowning, you see, with fierce pleasure, as though she were chewing a delicious piece of meat. So then Mary and all the children were grinning, because they knew instinctively what the frown of an old black woman meant.

In that incandescent moment, Mary had come to love Odessa Williams.

And the marvelous thing that had begun could only grow more marvelous still.

For I whispered, "Dee Dee," and the innocent child glanced at me, and I said, "Dee Dee, 'Silent Night.'"

Dear Dee Dee! That girl, as dark as the shadows around her, stroked the very air as though it were a chime of glass. (Dee Dee, I love you!) So high she soared on her crystal voice, so long she held the notes, that the rest of the children hummed and harmonized all unconsciously, and they began to sway together. "Round yon virgin, mother and child . . ."

Odessa's eyes flew open to see the thing that was happening around her. She looked, then she raised her long, long arms; and then lying on her back, the old woman began to direct the music. Odessa Williams gathered all her children and urged them to fly, and sent them on a celestial flight to glory, oh! These were not children anymore. These were the stars. Their voices ascended on fountains of light to become the very hosts of heaven—so high, so bright and holy and high. *Jesus, Lord, at thy birth!* So beautiful.

And then that woman brought them down again, by meek degrees to the earth again, and to this room and to her bedside; and there they stood, perfectly still, smiling in silence and waiting. How could anyone move immediately after such a wonder?

Nor did Odessa disappoint them. For then she began, in a low and smoky voice, to preach.

"Oh, children—you my choir," Odessa whispered. "Oh, choir—you my children for sure. An' listen to me," she whispered intently. She caught them one by one on the barb of her eye. "Ain' no one stand in front of you for goodness, no! You the bes', babies. You the absolute *best.*"

The children gazed at her, and the children believed her completely: they were the best. And my Mary, too, believed what she was hearing, heart and soul.

"Listen to me," Odessa said. "When you sing, wherever you go to sing, look down to the front row of the people who come to hear you sing. There's alluz an empty seat there. See it?" The children nodded. They saw it. "Know what that empty space is?" The children shook their heads. "It's me," she said, and they nodded. "It's me," she whispered in the deep orange light. "'Cause I alluz been with you children. An' whenever you sing, I'm goin' to be with you still. An' you know how I can say such a mackulous thing?"

They waited to know. She lowered her voice, and she told them. "Why, 'cause we in Jesus," she whispered the mystery. "Babies, babies, we be in the hand of Jesus, old ones, young ones, and us and you together. Jesus, he hold us in his hand, and ain' no one goin' to snatch us out. Jesus, he don' never let one of us go. Never. Not ever—"

So spoke Odessa, and then she fell silent. So said the woman with such conviction and such fierce love, that the children rolled tears from their open eyes, and they were not ashamed. They reached over and patted the bones of her body beneath the blankets.

Mary's eyes too were glistening. The woman had won my daughter. In that incandescent moment, Mary had come to love Odessa Williams. She slipped her soft hand toward the bed and touched the tips of Odessa's fingers, and she smiled and cried at once. For this is the power of a wise love wisely expressed: to transfigure a heart, suddenly, forever.

ON TUESDAY, the twenty-second of December, Odessa Williams died.

Gaines Funeral Home had less than a day to prepare her body, because the wake would take place on Wednesday evening. The funeral itself had to be scheduled for Thursday morning. She would be buried, then, on Christmas Eve Day.

Not brutally, but somewhat busily at lunch on Wednesday, I mentioned to my children that Miz Williams had died. They were eating soup. This was not an unusual piece of news in our household: the congregation had its share of elderly.

I scarcely noticed, then, that Mary stopped eating and stared at her bowl of soup.

I wiped my mouth and rose from the table.

"Dad?"

I was trying to remember what time the children should be at church to rehearse the Christmas program. Timing was everything. I wanted to give them a last instruction before I left.

"Dad?"

One thirty! "Listen—Mom will drive you to church at one fifteen. Can you all be ready then?"

"Dad?"

"Mary, what?" She was still staring at the soup, large eyes lost behind her hair.

"Is it going to snow tomorrow?" she said.

"What? I don't know. How would I know that?"

"It shouldn't snow," she said.

"You always wanted snow at Christmas."

In a tiny voice she whispered, "I want to go to the funeral."

Well, then that was it: she was considering what to wear against the weather. I said, "Fine," and left.

THURSDAY CAME grey and hard and cold and windless. It grudged the earth a little light and made no shadow. The sky was sullen, draining color from the grass and the naked trees. I walked to church in the morning.

We have a custom in our congregation: always, before a funeral service begins, we set the casket immediately in front of the chancel and leave it open about an hour. People come for a final viewing of the body, friends who couldn't attend the wake, acquaintances on their way to work, strangers out of the past, memories, stories that will never be told. The dead one lies the same for all who gaze at her, infinitely patient. So people enter the church, and they creep up the aisle, and they look, and they think, and they leave again.

And so it was that on Christmas Eve at eleven in the morning I discovered Mary outside the door. In fact, she was standing on the sidewalk while her mother parked the car. She was staring at the sullen sky.

"Mary?" I said. "Are you coming in?"

She glanced at me. Then she whispered, "Dad?" as though the news were dreadful. "It's going to snow."

It looked very likely to snow. The air was still, the whole world bleak and waiting. I could have agreed with her.

"Dad?" she repeated more urgently, probing me with large eyes—but what was I supposed to do? "It's going to snow!" she said.

"Come in, Mary. We don't have time to talk. Come in."

She entered the church ahead of me and climbed the steps in the narthex, then she started up the aisle toward the casket. She was seven years old. She was determined. Though robed and ready to preach, and though people sat face-forward on either side, I followed her.

Mary hesitated as she neared the chancel—but then took a final step and stopped.

She looked down into the casket. "Oh, no," she murmured, and I looked to see what she was seeing.

Odessa's eyes seemed closed with glue, her lips too pale, her color another shade than her own, a false, woody color. Her skin seemed pressed into its patience. And the bridge of her nose suffered a set of glasses. Had Odessa worn glasses? Yes, sometimes. But these were perched on her face a little askew, so that one became aware of them for the first time. Someone else had put them there. What belonged to the lady any more, and what did not?

These were my speculations.

Mary had her own.

The child was reaching her hand toward the tips of Odessa's fingers, fingers like sticks of chalk; but she paused and didn't touch them. Suddenly she bent down and pressed her cheek to the fingers, then pulled back and stood erect.

"Dad!" she hissed. Mary turned and looked at me and did not blink but began to cry. "Dad!" she whispered, accusing, "It's going to snow, and Miz Williams is so cold." Immediately the tears were streaming down her face. "Dad!" she wept. "They can't put Miz Williams in the grave today. It's going to snow on her grave. It's going to snow on Miz Williams—"

All at once Mary stepped forward and buried her face in my robes. I felt the pressure of her forehead against my chest—and I was her father again, no pastor, and my own throat grew thick.

"Dad," sobbed Mary. "Dad, Dad, it's Christmas *Eve*!"

How do I comfort these tears? What do I say?

I said nothing.

I knelt down. I took my Mary's face between my hands but couldn't hold her gaze. I gathered her to myself and hugged her tightly, hugged her hard, hugged her until the sobbing passed from her body; and then I released her.

> "*Dad!*" she whispered, accusing, "It's going to snow, and Miz Williams is so cold."

I watched her go back down the aisle like a poker soldier. She turned in a pew and sat with her mother. I saw that her lips were pinched into a terrible knot. No crying anymore. No questions anymore. Why should she ask questions when there no answers given?

So: the funeral. And so: the sermon. And so I was the pastor again.

Later, at Oak Hill cemetery, the people stood in great coats round the casket, shivering. My breath made ghosts in the air as I read of dust and ashes returning to dust and ashes. Mary said not a word nor held her mother's hand nor looked at me—except once.

When we turned from the grave she hissed, "Dad!" Her blue eyes flashing, she pointed at the ground. Then she pointed at the sky. At the roots of the grasses was a fine, white powder; in heaven was a darker powder coming down. It was snowing.

WE HAVE SEVERAL CUSTOMS—in our church and in my family—on Christmas Eve: as to the church, we celebrate the evening always with a children's pageant of the birth of Jesus. There never was the pageant in which my children didn't participate. As for my family, we always open our Christmas presents after the pageant is over, when the glow is still upon us, when Thanne and I can watch the children and enjoy their joy. Nothing is dearer to me than the purity of their gladness then, the undiscordant music of their laughter then.

And nothing could grieve me more, than that one of my children should be sad and lose the blessings of these customs.

Therefore, I worried terribly for Mary all Thursday through. As it happened, she was to be *the* Mary of the pageant, the Virgin, the mother of the infant Jesus.

We drove to church. The snow lay a loose inch on the ground. It swirled in snow-devils at the backs of the cars ahead of us. It held the grey light of the city near the earth, though this was now the night, and heaven was oblique in darkness. Surely, the snow covered Odessa's grave as well, a silent, seamless sheet.

These, I suppose, were Mary's thoughts, that the snow was cold on a new-dug grave. But Mary's thoughts confused with mine.

The rooms of the church were filled with light and noise, transfigured utterly from the low, funereal whispers of the morning. Black folk laughed. Parents stood in knots of conversation. Children darted, making ready for their glad performance, each in a different stage of dress, some in blue jeans, some in the robes of the shepherds two millennia and twenty lands away. Children were breathless and punchy. But Mary and I moved like spirits through this company, unnoticed and unnoticing. I was filled with her sorrow, while she seemed simply empty.

In time the wildness subsided. The actors huddled in their proper places. I sat with the congregation, two-thirds back on the right hand side. The lights in the sanctuary dimmed to darkness. The chancel glowed a yellow illumination. The pageant began, and soon my daughter stood with pinched lips, central to it all.

"My soul," said Mary, both Marys before a little Elizabeth—but she spoke so softly that few could hear, and my own soul suffered for her— "My soul," she murmured, "magnifies the Lord, and my spirit rejoices in God my Savior—"

And so: the child was surviving. But she was not rejoicing.

Some angels came and giggled and sang and left.

A decree went out.

Another song was sung.

And then three figures moved into the floodlit chancel: Joseph and Mary—and one other child, a sort of innkeeper-stage manager who carried the manger, a wooden trough filled with old straw and a floppy doll in diapers.

The pageant proceeded, but I lost the greater part of it in watching my daughter.

For Mary stuck out her bottom lip and began to frown on the manger in front of her—to frown fiercely, not at all like the devout and beaming parent she was supposed to portray. At the *manger* she was staring, which stood precisely where Odessa's casket had sat that morning. She frowned so hard, blacking her eyes in such deep shadow, that I thought she would break into tears again, and my mind raced over things to do when she couldn't control herself any longer.

But Mary did not cry.

Instead, while shepherds watched over their flocks by night, my Mary played a part that no one had written into the script. Slowly she slipped her hand into the manger and touched the doll in diapers. She lifted its arm on the tip of her pointed finger, then let it drop. *What are you thinking, Mary?* All at once, as though she'd made a sudden decision, she yanked the doll out by its toes, and stood up, and clumped down the chancel steps, the doll like a dishrag at her side. People made mild, maternal sounds in their throats. The rhythm of a certain angel faltered. *Mary, where are you going? What are you doing?* I folded my hands at my chin and yearned to hold her, hide her, protect her from anything, from folly and from sorrow. But she carried the doll to the darkened sacristy on the right and disappeared through its door. *Mary? Mary!*

In a moment the child emerged carrying nothing at all. Briskly she returned to the manger, up three steps as light as air, and down she knelt, and she gazed upon the empty straw with her palms together like the first Mary after all, full of adoration. And her face—Mary, my Mary, your face was radiant then!

O Mary, how I love you!

Not suddenly, but with a rambling, stumbling charge, there was in the chancel a multitude of the proudest heavenly host, praising God and shouting, "Glory to God in the highest!" But Mary knelt unmoved among them, and her seven-year face was smiling, and there was the flash of tears upon her cheeks, but they were not unhappy, and the manger, open, empty, seemed the receiver of them.

"Silent night, holy night—" All of the children were singing. "All is calm, all is bright—" The deeper truck-rumble of older voices joined them. "Round yon virgin mother and child—" The whole congregation was singing. Candlelight was passing hand to hand. A living glow spread everywhere throughout the church. And then the shock of recognition, and the soft flight followed: Dee Dee Lawrence allowed her descant voice its high, celestial freedom, and she flew. "Holy infant, so tender and mild—" *Mary, what do you see? What do you know that your father could not tell you? Mary, mother of the infant Jesus, teach me too.*

"Sleep in heavenly peace—" Having touched the crystal heaven, Dee Dee descended. The congregation sighed. Everybody sang: "Sleep in heavenly peace."

MARY SAT IMMEDIATELY BESIDE ME in the car as we drove home. A sifting snow made cones below the streetlights. It blew lightly across the windshield and closed us in a cotton privacy. I had been driving in silence.

Mary said, "Dad?"

I said, "What?"

She said, "Dad, Jesus wasn't in the manger. That wasn't Jesus. That was a doll." Ah, Mary, so you have the eyes of a realist now? And there is no pretending any more? It was a doll indeed. So death reveals realities—

"Dad?"

"What?"

She said, "Jesus, he doesn't *have* to be in the manger, does he? He goes back and forth, doesn't he? I mean, he came from heaven, and he was borned right here, but then he went back to heaven again, and because he came and went he's coming and going *all* the time—right?"

"Right," I whispered. Teach me, child. It is so good to hear you talk again.

"The manger is empty," Mary said. And then she said more gravely, "Dad, Miz Williams' box is empty too. I figured it out. We don't have to worry about the snow." She stared out the windshield a moment, then whispered the next thing as softly as if she were peeping at presents: "It's only a doll in her box. It's like a big doll, Dad, and we put it away today. I figured it out. If Jesus can cross, if Jesus can go across, then Miz Williams, she crossed the same way too, with Jesus—"

Jesus, he don't never let one of us go. Never.

"Dad?" said Mary, who could ponder so much in her heart. "Why are you crying?"

Babies, babies, we be in the hand of Jesus, old ones, young ones, us and you together. Jesus, he hold us in his hand, and ain' no one goin' to snatch us out. Jesus, he don't never let one of us go. Never. Not ever—

"Because I have nothing else to say," I said to her. "I haven't had the words for some time now."

"Dad?"

"What?"

"Don't cry. I can talk for both of us."

IT ALWAYS WAS; it always will be; it was in the fullness of time when the Christ child first was born; it was in 1981 when my daughter taught me the times and the crossing of times on Christmas Eve; it is in every celebration of Christ's own crossing; and it shall be forever—that this is the power of a wise love wisely expressed: to transfigure the heart, suddenly, forever. ✣

Popular author, storyteller and lecturer, Walter Wangerin Jr. lives with his wife Thanne in an old farmhouse outside Valparaiso, Indiana. In addition to his writing, storytelling, and lecturing, Wangerin is the speaker for the radio program "Lutheran Vespers."

Illustration by Gail Hicks, represented by Sharon Morris Associates, San Francisco, California.

LET THE STABLE STILL ASTONISH

Let the stable still astonish:
straw-dirt floor, dull eyes,
dusty flanks of donkeys, oxen;
crumbling, crooked walls;
no bed to carry that pain.
And then, the child,
rag-wrapped, laid to cry
in a trough.

Who would have chosen this?
Who would have said: "Yes,
let the God of all the heavens and earth
be born here, in this place"?

Who but the same God
who stands in the darker, fouler rooms
of our hearts
and says, "Yes,
let the God of Heaven and Earth
be born here—
in *this* place."

LESLIE LEYLAND FIELDS

Leslie Leyland Fields lives in Kodiak, Alaska, with her
husband, four children and a pair of bald eagles that soar
past her window while she writes poems. Her work has
appeared in numerous journals and periodicals.
Illustration and border by Dan Reed.

A NIGHT THE STARS DANCED FOR JOY

BOB HARTMAN

A READ-ALOUD STORY

he old shepherd, the shepherd's wife and the shepherd boy lay on their backs on top of the hill.

Their hands were folded behind their heads, and their feet stretched out in three directions like points on a ompass. Their day's work was done. Their sheep had dropped off to sleep. And they had run out of things to say.

So they just lay there on top of that hill and stared lazily into the night sky.

It was a clear night. There were no clouds for shy stars to hide behind. And the bolder stars? For some reason, they seemed to be shining more proudly than even the old shepherd could remember.

Suddenly, what must have been the boldest star of all came rushing across the sky, dancing from one horizon to the other and showing off its sparkling serpent's tail.

"Shooting star," said the boy dreamily. "Make a wish."

The old shepherd and his wife said nothing. They were too old for games and too tired, tonight, even to say so.

But they were not too old for wishing.

The old shepherd fixed his eyes on a cluster of stars that looked like a great bear. And he thought about the cluster of scars on his leg—jagged reminders of a battle he'd fought with a real bear long ago. A battle to save his sheep. He had been young and strong then. He'd won that battle.

There were other scars, too, mapped out like a hundred roads across his back. Souvenirs of his battles with that Great Bear, Rome. The land of Israel belonged to his people, not to the Roman invaders who were devouring it with their tyranny and taxes. So why should he bow politely to Roman soldiers and surrender his sheep for their banquets? Greedy tyrants. Uniformed thieves. That's what they were—the lot of them. And even their claw-sharp whips would not change his mind.

And so, even though he said nothing, the old shepherd made a wish. He wished for someone to save him. From violence. From greed. From bears.

The shepherd's wife had her eyes shut. This was the hardest time of the day for her. The time when there was nothing to do but try to fall asleep. The time when the wind always carried voices back to her. Her voice and her mother's. Angry, bitter voices. Voices hurling words that hurt. Words she wished she'd never spoken. Words she couldn't take back now, because her mother was dead. And there was no chance to say she was sorry.

And so, even though she said nothing, the shepherd's wife silently wished for peace, for an end to those bitter voices on the wind.

The shepherd boy grew tired of waiting. "All right," he said finally. "*I'll* make a wish then. I wish . . . I wish . . . I wish something interesting would happen for a change. Something exciting. I'm tired of just sitting on this hill night after night. I want something to laugh about. To sing and dance about."

The old shepherd turned to look at his wife.

The shepherd's wife opened her eyes and shook her head.

But before either of them could lecture their son about being satisfied with what he had, something happened. Something that suggested the shepherd boy just might get his wish.

Like tiny white buds blossoming into gold flowers, the stars began to swell and spread, until their edges bled together and the sky was filled with a glowing blanket of light. And then that blanket of light began to shrink and gather itself into a brilliant, blinding ball that hung above the shepherds and left the rest of the sky black and empty.

Wide-eyed and slack-jawed, the shepherds dared not move. The wind had stopped. And the shepherds lay glued to the hillside, staring into that light. They watched it slowly change again. Shining rays stretched into arms. Legs kicked out like white beams. And a glowing face blinked bright and burning. The light sprouted wings. It took the shape of an angel. And it spoke.

"Don't be afraid," the angel said. "But sing and dance for joy! I have good news for you.

Today, in Bethlehem, your Savior was born—the Special One whom God promised to send you. Here's the proof: if you go to Bethlehem, you will find the baby wrapped in cloths and lying in a feed trough."

The shepherds were still too shocked to speak. But that didn't keep them from thinking.

"Don't be afraid?" thought the old shepherd. "He's got to be kidding."

"A baby in a feed trough?" thought the shepherd's wife. "Why even our own son got better treatment than that."

"Sing and dance for joy?" thought the shepherd boy. "Now that's more like it!"

And, as if in answer to the boy's thought, the angel threw his arms and legs wide, like the first step in some heavenly jig. But instead, he flung himself—could it be?—into a thousand different pieces of light, pieces that scattered themselves across the dark blue of the night and landed where the stars had been. Pieces that turned into angels themselves, singing a song that the shepherds had never heard before, to a tune that had been humming in their heads forever.

"Glory to God in the highest!" the angels sang. "And peace on earth to all."

Some plucked at lyres. Some blew trumpets. Some beat drums. Some banged cymbals. There were dancers, as well—spinning and whirling, larking and leaping across the face of the midnight moon.

Finally, when the music could get no louder, when the singers could sing no stronger, when the dancers could leap no higher, when the shepherds' mouths and eyes could open no further, everything came to a stop.

As quickly as the angels had come, they were gone. The sky was silent and filled once more with twinkling stars. The shepherds lay there for a moment, blinking and rubbing their eyes.

At last the old shepherd struggled to his feet. "Well," he said, "looks like we'd better find this baby."

The shepherd's wife pulled herself up, shook the grass off her robe and ran her fingers absently through her hair.

The shepherd boy leaped eagerly to his feet and shouted "Hooray!"

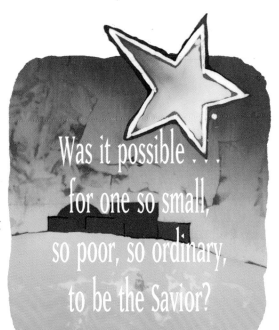

Was it possible . . . for one so small, so poor, so ordinary, to be the Savior?

When they got to Bethlehem, things were just as the angel had said. A husband and a young mother. And a baby in a feed trough. A family much like the shepherd's, in fact. Was it possible, the old man wondered, for one so small, so poor, so ordinary, to be the Savior? The Promised One?

Then he told the young mother about the angels. And that's when he knew. It was the look in her eyes. The look that said, "How wonderful!" but also, "I'm not surprised." There was something special going on here. The angels knew it. The mother knew it. And now the shepherd and his family knew it, too.

Well," said the boy as they made their way back to the hill, "my wish came true. Too bad you didn't make a wish."

The old shepherd said nothing. But he ran one finger gently along his scars. Was he imagining things, or were they smaller now?

The shepherd's wife said nothing. She was listening. There were no bitter voices on the wind now. There were songs—heaven songs—and the cry of a newborn child.

"Glory to God in the highest!" she shouted suddenly.

"And peace to everyone on earth!" the old shepherd shouted back.

Then the shepherd boy shouted, too— "Hooray!"—and danced like an angel for joy.

o Christmas wishes come true? They did for the shepherd boy. In the second chapter of Luke you can read the original account of that angel visit.

But what about the old shepherd's wish for someone to save him from the bears of violence and greed? When the baby in the feed trough grew up, he talked about loving others as you want to be loved. He taught that there are more important things than getting as much money as you can. And a lot of violent and greedy people listened to what he said and changed their ways.

And how about the shepherd's wife and her wish for peace? Jesus made that wish come true as well. He explained to people how important it was to forgive those who hurt you. And when he died on the cross for all the wrong and hurtful things other people had done, he made God's own forgiveness available to women and men and children of all times.

CHiLDReN, iMAGiNAtiON, AND CHRistMAS ANGeLS

INTERVIEWS BY BOB HARTMAN

Imagine you were one of those shepherds on the hills of Bethlehem the night Jesus was born. Imagine that the Christmas angels appeared to you. What did they look like? How did they sound? How did their surprise visit make you feel?

Answers to those questions were provided by young time travelers ranging in age from six to fourteen. Some saw tiny, fairy-sized creatures; others imagined enormous heavenly beings. Some pictured bright balls of light;

and at least one girl described an angel that bore striking resemblance to Barbie! But for all the wonderful differences, in almost every case, the children saw in the angels an expression of God's own beauty, goodness, and love.

Travel back in time yourself to ancient Bethlehem. Lie back on that hillside and stare into the night sky. Marry your heart with your imagination and look at Christmas angels through the eyes of a child.

Danielle McInnes, 8

If you are lucky enough to see an angel, she would have beautiful, light, sheer pink wings. She would have long, shiny, shimmering blond hair. She would be as beautiful on the outside as she is on the inside.

DANIELLE MCINNES, 8

I thought my eyes were playing tricks on me. I rubbed my eyes three times. I saw a small ball of light in the sky. It had wings, and it spoke to me in a small, gentle voice.

CHRISTINA VANDEN BOSCHE, 10

A burst of light nearly blinded us. As my vision cleared, I saw the angels. Their hair shimmered like waves of grain in the summer breeze. Their eyes were blue as the sky and bright as stars. A sweet fragrance of jasmine and roses filled the air.
I felt we were on the verge of a whole new era, an age where love would overcome sin.

JUDITH MARIE THOMAS, 12

I think angels are HUGE.

KELLY ALLSHOUSE, 7

Kevin Crummie, 6

I didn't have to *think* about how an angel looks, I *knew* how it looks. An angel has gold, glittering robes. And it has golden wings. And it has a gold circle above its head that's kind of floating there, like someone's holding it. Now that's an angel!

KEVIN CRUMMIE, 6

An angel has a headband with a star and wings and a beautiful brown dress and brown hair. The angels are nice . . . well, *very* nice. And there are boy angels, too, just like the girls.

DANIELLE MUSHINSKY, 8

Angels are nice and kind to everyone. They are so loving you want to hug them. But when you try, your arms go right through them.

CAITLIN CRUMMIE, 12

34

Christopher Wojciechowski, 8

Mark Ford, 9

They look like a white light, and they have gold wings and crowns, and they sing.

CHRISTOPHER WOJCIECHOWSKI, 8

He was very tall, with long golden hair. His bright blue eyes held a joy too great not to share. But I think his wings were the most beautiful thing about him. They seemed to be made of sunbeams, and a dazzling radiance came from them.

MAGGIE ORR, 11

The wind began to blow fiercely, sending chills throughout my body. Then everything went calm, and a great pure light filled the sky. When the first angel touched the ground, a stream formed. When the second angel touched the ground, grass began to grow, and everything became green and beautiful. The angels were dressed in the same pure light. They glowed from head to toe like the stars.

REBECCA DUNHAM, 14

Angels love shepherds.

CHAD LOWE, 7

The angels had a big, big, big, big smile on their faces.

MARK FORD, 9

What an angel looks like to me . . .

    Clothes: a wavy gold and silver dress

    Face: brown hair, brown eyes, smooth skin

    Size: 5' 10"

    Jewelry: rings on all fingers and a special necklace

    Shoes: gold with a diamond on it

    Legs: skinny and smooth

STEPHANIE OBRINGER, 9

Bob Hartman, the compiler of this article and author of "A Night the Stars Danced for Joy," is a writer, minister, and professional storyteller. The thoughts about Christmas angels were collected on his storytelling encounters with groups of children in the Pittsburgh area. Hartman lives with his wife and two children in Ben Avon, Pennsylvania.

Illustrations were redrawn by Merritt Meyer, age 8, of Robbinsdale, Minnesota. This is Merritt's first published artwork.

THE EXPECTATION OF ANGELS

They used to be commonplace—
Jacob wrestled one
and Milton launched whole armies.
Even Mary seemed more surprised by the message
than the messenger. Angels trooped
through dreams and tramped along roads.
Though they were not always recognized,
they were accepted—almost expected.

But today imagine the visitation of angels:
fingerprints, social security numbers,
the Audubon Society inspecting
wings, the Pope finding them undisciplined,
the World Council of Churches voting
support, but no expectation of funding.

Still, they come flapping and laughing
above our Christmas trees,
posing for plastic ornaments (as expected),
singing in the Harlem Boys Choir,
others humming in a rock group's
bass guitar, some residing
in suburbia; Powers, Thrones,
Seraphim, their wings close-pressed
beneath their business suits
and always ready to tell us
"Do not be afraid."
—NOLA GARRETT

Nola Garrett is an English professor and the wife of a Lutheran pastor in Wesleyville, Pennsylvania. Her poems have appeared in numerous periodicals, and she recently has had her first book of poetry published. "The Expectation of Angels" is drawn from material in biblical accounts of angel visitations and Milton's *Paradise Lost*.

The photo illustration was created using a series of pin-hole camera exposures. Minneapolis artist-photographer Joel Sheagren explains his choice of technique: "After reading the poem over and over, it made sense that the illustration lean toward the abstract, making the angels slightly harder to find—as they are in everyday life."

Border illustration by Dan Reed.

THE GIFT

MARILYN KOETZ

I don't want a thing for Christmas," Aunt Agatha said sternly, "not a thing. Do I make myself clear?'

"But Aunt Agatha, you know Dan and I will get you something," I cajoled. "After all, you're his favorite aunt."

Her rigid posture and frosty expression told me I had gone too far. I knew she had interpreted my intended-to-be-kind remark as patronizing.

"How old are you, Kathleen?" she asked.

"Twenty."

"And exactly how long have you and my nephew Daniel been married?"

"Seven months and thirteen days . . ."

"Spare me the hours and minutes." (Did I detect the faintest glimmer of a smile?) "You are new to this family. I am extremely fond of Daniel. Nevertheless, there is not one thing I need or want. Don't waste your time or money on a gift for me."

I could feel myself blushing. "I—I don't know what to say."

"You needn't say anything. I don't mean to be unkind, just explicit. Will you have more tea?"

"No, thank you." Embarrassed, I stood up. To cover my confusion, I pretended to be engrossed in drawing on my thick wool gloves. "I really stopped by to invite you for Christmas Eve," I said hopefully. (I *would* win over this austere woman.) "Since Dan and I moved to Grandfather's farm, we have lots of room to entertain. I love everything about that house! There are so many rooms, and the walnut woodwork is beautiful."

"I'm pleased that you're so fond of Papa's home. I grew up there, so there are many memories."

"Living there gives Dan and me a sense of family."

"The family appreciates Daniel and you acting as caretakers. Papa will never leave the nursing home alive, and that's difficult. But having family at the farm eases the pain a little. We are grateful to you."

"We're the ones who are grateful. I've quit my part-time job, and I'll be going back to school winter quarter. With no rent to pay, we can manage that. "

There was an awkward silence. After a few seconds I cleared my throat. "You haven't said you'll come Christmas Eve."

"Christmas Eve. Yes, well . . . This year, you see . . ."

Nervously, I looked out the window at the softly falling snowflakes. Suddenly my Christmas spirit overwhelmed me. "*Please* come, Aunt Agatha. We especially want *you* to come. Really! No one can take your place with us."

"Why, thank you, Kathleen. Then I'd be delighted to come—if you're really sure you want *me* this year." Suddenly she was warm and friendly.

"Oh, we do, we do! I've always loved Christmas, and this year it will be especially memorable at the farm. We have a candle in every window, and there's room for a huge tree in the front bay window."

She smiled. "It *is* a remarkable place, isn't it? Especially during the holidays. And now, what shall I bring: my whiskey cake or my Irish soda bread? . . . Oh, I'll just bring both."

"Why, thank you, Aunt Agatha."

She walked me to the door, and to my astonishment, delivered a cool kiss to my cheek. "I'll see you on Christmas Eve, then. About what time?"

"Seven. We thought we'd have the tree and gifts first and then a late Christmas Eve supper."

"That's our family tradition," she said with satisfaction as she closed the door behind me.

Snow was falling in slow motion—beautiful, lazy flakes that settled, cozy as a quilt, on the chilled landscape. I got in my car humming "White Christmas." I always looked forward to this season above all others, and this year I had a new husband, a new home, and a whole new family to make things even merrier. I was eager to meet all Dan's relatives. Because we had married in my hometown—fifteen hundred miles away from Dan's—only his parents, two sisters, and their families had attended the wedding. Now, during the holidays, I would get to know the relatives I'd met only casually since our marriage.

The car radio was playing "Silent Night," and the car's tires were crunching deliciously through accumulating snowdrifts. I didn't have a glimmer of the disaster I had just set in motion.

Just one more stop—at Aunt Violet's—and then I'd go home and make Dan a big pot of chili. We'd eat it in front of the fireplace.

Aunt Violet took a few minutes to answer the door. "Why, hello, Kathleen. Are you having trouble with the sweater you're knitting for Daniel?"

"I did bring it, Aunt Violet," I said as she led me to the big Queen Anne chair in her living room. "Would you mind checking to see if you can find my mistake?"

She put on her glasses, took the sweater from me and expertly went over my work.

"Well, yes. I see what you did. I'll just unravel this and then I'll knit a few rows to get you started again."

I laughed. "I think *you're* really knitting this sweater. Every few days you have to unravel my mistakes and then knit 'a few rows to get me started again.'"

"We all have to learn," she said companionably. "Would you like something to eat or drink?"

"No thanks." How she could make those knitting needles fly! "I'm going home to make chili. I just stopped to tell you that Dan and I are having Christmas Eve this year. Won't it be lovely at the farmhouse? You *will* come, won't you, Aunt Violet?"

"Of course I will, dear. I want to see Dan's face when he opens this sweater! He doesn't even know I taught you how to knit. Oh, and I always bring my cranberry relish and sweet pickle slices."

The telephone rang and she put down Dan's sweater to answer it. I waited a few minutes, then folded the soft wool carefully into my knitting bag and motioned toward the door, indicating I would slip out quietly while she talked. She waved goodbye, smiled, and continued her conversation.

Later that evening, Dan and I sat beside a crackling apple-wood fire eating chili. I knew it was tasty this time because he refilled his bowl three times.

"Delicious, Kathy. It wasn't burned this time—not even scorched!"

I threw a pillow at him. "I burned it *one time*, you chauvinist pig."

He ducked and laughed. "So what did my beautiful young wife do today—besides make mouth-watering chili?"

"I worked on your Christmas present. Oh Dan, I can't wait to give it to you!"

"What color is it, Kathy? Is it bigger than a bread box?"

"You could never, ever guess what it is, even with clues. Oh, and I went shopping, and then I called on Aunt Agatha and Aunt Violet and invited them both for Christmas Eve."

"You *what*?" Dan put down his bowl and stared at me.

I was puzzled by his tone. "What in the world's the matter with you? I invited them for Christmas Eve dinner. Why are you so excited?"

"Kathy, they haven't spoken to each other for eleven years!"

"No!" Now it was my turn to be startled.

"How could you do such a thing? I can't believe it."

"But Dan," I protested, "I didn't know. No one ever told me."

"How could you be a member of this family for seven months and not know that? You've met them both. Surely we must have mentioned . . ."

> ## Wonderful. My first *faux pas* as Dan's wife would ruin Christmas for my new family.

"No one told me, Dan! I could never forget a thing like that."

"Well, what did Aunt Agatha say? What did Aunt Violet say? Weren't they upset when you told them they were both invited?"

"They both said 'yes.' I didn't specifically mention to either of them that I'd invited the other. I told each of them we were having Christmas Eve this year. They both know that means the whole family."

"No way! They come on alternate years. This year it's Aunt Violet's turn. She's expecting to come. I can't believe Aunt Agatha accepted. Are you sure you didn't misunderstand her?"

"She's bringing her whiskey cake and Irish soda bread."

"She *is* coming. I can't believe it. She couldn't have gotten the impression that Aunt Violet won't be here, could she?"

"I don't see how . . . Oh Dan, oh darling!" I suddenly remembered urging Aunt Agatha to come, telling her no one could take her place. No wonder she had become so warm and friendly. She thought I had deliberately excluded Aunt Violet because I preferred her company on Christmas Eve. I explained to Dan, ending with, "What should we do?"

"I have no idea what *you* should do."

"Dan! You can't desert me at a time like this."

He looked at me fondly. "My poor little Kathy. Let me think a minute. A more mature mind is needed for something this serious." (My wise, super-mature, twenty-seven-year-old husband!)

"Oh? Should I call your mother, then?" I asked innocently. I had endured a lot of teasing about being seven years younger than Dan.

"Darned if I can figure it out. Why *don't* you call my mother in the morning? Maybe she can suggest something. She's tried to get the aunts together for years. The holidays are always so hard on Dad with the aunts feuding. Maybe she'll have an idea—but I doubt it."

Wonderful. My first *faux pas* as Dan's wife would ruin Christmas for my new family. And just when I'd been feeling so married, so adult.

I phoned Dan's mother as soon as he'd left for work the next morning. I explained the situation and held my breath.

"Oh Kathy, I'm so sorry we let you in for this. I can't imagine how we could have forgotten to tell you about the aunts. I guess we've all become so used to the situation we don't think about it anymore. Oh dear! Oh my! And they are both coming, you say?"

"*Couldn't* they both come?" I asked. There are thirty-two people invited, with all the cousins and their children. Maybe I could keep them separated somehow."

My mother-in-law is tactful. "Well, I don't know, Kathy. Do you think you could?"

Of course I couldn't. The farmhouse is large, but we would all be together in the parlor and dining room for the festivities. "Oh, I could just cut my heart out!" I moaned.

She laughed in sympathy. "That seems a bit dramatic. Unfortunately, the only suggestion I can offer is that you tell Agatha the truth."

"But how can I? She thinks I asked her *especially*. I hate to hurt her like that."

"Maybe you could tell Violet then."

"But it's her turn," I said, trying not to whine. "That would be cruel. What did they get so mad about in the first place?"

"It was such a little thing, really. As a matter of fact, it was our family Christmas Eve celebration that started it. Violet was having the family that year. She's the artsy-

craftsy one, so she hand-painted little invitations and mailed them. I talked to Agatha on the telephone that Christmas Eve afternoon and mentioned how attractive the little cards were. Agatha said she hadn't received one. I said, 'Well, you two talk on the phone every day. You helped her plan the dinner. Why would she think she needed to send you a mailed invitation?' I didn't think any more about it. That night, though, Agatha didn't come. I told Violet why Agatha was upset, so she called her. It had never occurred to Violet to send her sister a written invitation. Agatha was deeply offended. She said, 'You have one sister and one brother. Did you send your brother an invitation?' Violet said, 'Well, yes, but he has a family.' Agatha banged down the phone, and they haven't spoken since."

"And now I've gone and brought it all back up again. Just tell me what you think I should do, and I'll do it," I said desperately.

"Kathy dear, I think the only thing you can do is to tell Agatha exactly what happened. She knows it's Violet's year to come. She may be hurt, but it's the only solution I can think of. Do you think you can handle it?"

"I'll have to." *Please, please offer to call Aunt Agatha for me!*

After a few seconds she said, "Would you like me to call Agatha for you?"

I couldn't believe my ears when I heard myself say, "Thank you, but I think it's my responsibility." She seemed relieved. "Well, it's only twenty days until Christmas. I wouldn't wait too long."

That night I told Dan. I beamed when he said he respected me for deciding to handle the matter myself. I would call Aunt Agatha in the morning and get it over with.

The next day I put Christmas music on the stereo and baked cookies. It was gray and cold and windy outside. Inside, the farmhouse was warm and cozy and smelled of cinnamon. It was nineteen days until Christmas—quite a long time, really. Tomorrow I would call Aunt Agatha.

The days before the holidays were hectic. I finished Dan's sweater. I scrubbed the old wood floors in the parlor and polished the furniture. The house smelled of lemon oil. Dan's mother phoned to ask if I'd talked to Aunt Agatha yet. It was fifteen days until Christmas, and it had slipped my mind. I said I'd call her tomorrow for sure.

Ten days before Christmas, Dan and I rode the tractor through the farm to find a big evergreen for the bay window in the parlor. (Old farmhouses have such high ceilings.) We checked Grandfather's attic for tree ornaments and decorations and found we needed to buy very little. Dan was roping gold tinsel around the branches when he ran out.

"Did you remember to get more of this gold stuff?" he asked. "Oh, and speaking of remembering, you did remember to call Aunt Agatha, didn't you?"

"You must think I'm feeble-minded," I said scornfully, handing him the new plastic-wrapped gold tinsel roping. Imagine him thinking I would forget something as important as tree decorations. (I would positively *have* to call Aunt Agatha the very next day.)

One week before Christmas—seven days. I called all the relatives to check on who was bringing what. I addressed and mailed a card to everyone who had sent us one but who had not been on our list. I wrapped gifts while I hummed Christmas carols. Everything was right on schedule.

Three days before Christmas I awakened to the sound of sleet on the roof. After breakfast I took the turkey out of the freezer to thaw. I made the sauce for the baked ham. I decided to make yeast rolls from my mother's recipe. I listened to "Here Comes Santa Claus" on the radio. The weather forecast promised new snow for the

Tomorrow I would go see Aunt Agatha in person and throw myself on her mercy . . . *Last chance!*

holidays. There was really only one thing that still needed attention—one thing that I kept shoving to the back of my mind. And now, two days before Christmas Eve, my stomach churned as it stared me in the face.

Tomorrow I would go see Aunt Agatha in person and throw myself on her mercy. I could put it off no longer. It must be done. *Last chance!*

On Christmas Eve morning it was snowing. The world was white and glistening, the house fragrant with the smell of evergreens. The stately tree in the parlor was surrounded by gifts wrapped in gold, green, and white, with magnificent red bows. The candy dishes were filled with homemade fudge. As I roasted hazelnuts in the oven, I thought of my new red velvet dress hanging in the closet upstairs. I knew that tonight it would contrast vividly with my stark white, completely bloodless face. I had not contacted Aunt Agatha. It was too late. I tried to put it out of my mind. It was too late. There was nothing I could do now.

Christmas Eve. The snow is exquisite. The farmhouse smells of roasting ham, baking turkey, Christmas pine and burning apple wood. Aunt Violet and Dan's sisters and their families are here early to help. The children are starry-eyed and angel-perfect in their Christmas clothes. I have on my red dress, and I'm wearing the only-for-special-occasions Worth perfume that Dan loves. Aunt Violet comes in from the kitchen. She has taken off her apron.

"Everything's ready in the kitchen, Kathleen. Now it's my job to answer the front door."

"Oh, it's so cold, Aunt Violet. I'll do it."

"Nonsense! This is my job," she says firmly.

Dan looks at my face. He thinks I'm upset because I want to play hostess. "This is Kathy's first Christmas, Aunt Violet. Why don't you both welcome the new arrivals?"

The doorbell rings. I race Aunt Violet to the door. Dan's parents come in, loaded with packages. We kiss. We hug. We go to the parlor. Dan has Christmas tapes on the stereo. If ever there was a seemingly perfect, Christmas-card Christmas, it is here, now, in this place.

The doorbell rings a short, imperative blast. The very sound says "Aunt Agatha!" I think my heart has stopped. I arrive at the door just as Aunt Violet puts her hand on the knob. She opens the door. Aunt Agatha stands there holding her wrapped whiskey cake on a silver platter. The beribboned Irish soda bread is tucked under her arm.

The aunts stare at each other. They stare at me. I am stone and ice in my red dress. There is no movement, no sound. It seems as if the whole world has stopped. In the corner of my eye, I see the family gathering.

I look at Aunt Violet. Then at Aunt Agatha. My knees are shaking. Then, faintly, I hear the strains of "Hark the Herald Angels Sing" coming from the stereo. Suddenly I blurt out, "Peace on earth!"

Both aunts stand totally silent. The sounds of the carol float through the door. Suddenly Aunt Agatha drops the cake and bread just as Aunt Violet steps forward.

"Sister!" Aunt Agatha sobs as she throws her arms around Aunt Violet.

"Agatha!" Aunt Violet is weeping and embracing her sister at the same time.

Then the whole family surrounds them and everyone is laughing and crying and hugging and kissing. The stereo is now playing "Oh, Come, All Ye Faithful," and the children begin running through the house, wild with excitement.

Dan comes to put his arm around me with a strangely soft expression in his eyes. He puts his face next to me and inhales my perfume as he nuzzles my cheek. "Now, Kathy," he whispers in my ear, "you know perfectly well that Aunt Agatha told you *not* to give her a gift for Christmas." ◈

From her home in Columbus, Ohio, Marilyn Koetz writes stories about family life that can be appreciated by her husband, three children and seven grandchildren. "The Gift" is based on an incident that occurred in her family many years ago.

Illustration by Kara Fellows, Minneapolis, Minnesota.

LOOKING TOWARD CHRISTMAS

Advent again,
and the very stones are silent.

In the east, no star;
only shadows
and the threat of darkness.
We have run out of light,
and we wait in fear.

Still…

From the cosmic distance,
tentacles of brilliance probe,
seek us out, look for a dwelling place
among us.

CARYL PORTER

Caryl Porter lives in Duarte, California. She is a wife, mother, and grandmother who has written six published novels. The poem "Looking Toward Christmas" expresses her gratitude for God's supreme gift of love, year after year, despite our frailties and mistakes.

Photography ©Hans Strands/Tony Stone Images. Border illustration by Dan Reed.

MESSENGERS OF HIS BIRTH

PHILLIP GUGEL

Christmas Angels in Paintings by
the Master of Flémalle, Paul de Limbourg, and Hugo van der Goes

Reflecting the Gospel accounts of Luke and Matthew, where angels appear at key points in the Christmas events, these treasured paintings by two Flemish Renaissance masters and a medieval French illuminator capture the splendor of Christmas angels in three scenes surrounding the birth of Jesus.

MASTER OF FLÉMALLE

The archangel Gabriel, whose name means "God is my strength," plays the sole angelic role in *The Annunciation* from the Mérode Altarpiece by the Flemish Renaissance painter known as the Master of Flémalle.

He depicts Gabriel's visit to Mary against the background of an early fifteenth-century, middle-class Flemish home. The first known artist to set the Annunciation in a contemporary setting, he may have drawn on popular current accounts of the event, which placed it in a domestic interior.

Gabriel's majestic figure seems awkward in such a small room. He is not separated from the Virgin, as was often the case in earlier versions of the scene. Though he genuflects and salutes her, Mary seems absorbed in reading her prayer book, not yet aware of his presence.

The angel's face expresses a kindness and serenity we might hope to see if we met him; his hair is worn in a style popular among men of the artist's day. The voluminous alb draped with a long blue stole (blue was the traditional color for the Virgin) signifies Gabriel as the bearer of God's gracious message for Mary. Painted in hues reminiscent of an exotic parrot's plumage, the angel's wings symbolize a divine mission.

The Master of Flémalle used symbolism to allude to the implications of Mary's role as the bearer of God's grace to humankind. The extinguished candle on the table, for example, indicates that earthly light is overcome by heavenly light—the advent of God's Son—which Gabriel's announcement heralds. At least ten additional symbolic allusions are identifiable. The use of vividly painted objects—a lily, a ray of light, a washbasin—imbued with allusions to the Virgin and the Christ child's birth was an innovation in sacred art which the Master of Flémalle developed to the highest degree.

The Annunciation C. 1425
The Metropolitan Museum of Art, The Cloisters Collection, 1956. (56.70) Copyright © 1981 By The Metropolitan Museum of Art.

PAUL DE LIMBOURG

A trio of angels lauds Jesus' birth in the *Annunciation to the Shepherds*, a manuscript illumination adorning the page of a prayer book illustrated by Paul de Limbourg and two of his brothers. The illustration was commissioned by Jean, the Duke of Berry, perhaps the foremost art patron during the closing years of the medieval era in France.

Unlike the story in St. Luke's narrative, Paul's version takes place during the day. This detail suggests that the artist was familiar with a popular account of Jesus' birth in which three suns merged during the angels' visit to the shepherds.

Floating on a vivid blue cloud, the singing messengers hover so close to the herdsmen that the floating ends of their mantles almost touch them, unifying the figures. The pleasing, sophisticated colors in the angels and cloud draw our attention to the horizon and give the figures dominance over the landscape.

The shepherd's rose cowl repeats the hue of one angel's mantle and further unifies these earthly and heavenly beings. Though the shepherds seem surprised by their visitors, their elegant poses look out of character for simple, unlettered peasants.

Around the figures, a landscape punctuated with steep inclines, medieval spires, and miniature trees unfolds as a confining and crowded backdrop for the event. The illuminator's intent was to impart a courtly elegance and joyfulness to the scene, rather than accurately rendering the scale of animals, buildings, figures, and trees.

The artist's amusing inclusion of the dog with cocked ears, the goat scratching its head with a hind leg while its companion stretches to nibble at a branch, add a sense of liveliness and a touch of charm to his otherwise stately version of the angels' annunciation to the shepherds.

Annunciation to the Shepherds from *Les Belles Heures de Jean, Duc de Berry.* c. 1410–1413

HUGO VAN DER GOES

An excess of beautifully garbed angels adore the Christ-child in this *Nativity* by Hugo van der Goes. The scene adorns the main panel of his Portinari Altarpiece, a work overpowering in its complexity and size.

Four groups of angels are arranged at the ends of two diagonals intersecting the central figures of Mary and the Infant. In a departure from Luke's account, the child is shown nude, lying on the ground and emitting rays of light. Joseph and the shepherds form the points of a third diagonal through the scene.

In the first diagonal, a pair of angels in white albs complements its opposite in light blue albs. Five sumptuously vested, kneeling angels counter the two figures hovering above Joseph and Mary. A fifth group of four angels hovers near the top of the ruined stable. The artist did not include all these angels merely because he fancied them; the fifteen angels were a visual allusion to the Fifteen Joys of the Virgin, a medieval devotional practice recalling Mary's honored status.

The small size of the angels relative to that of the human figures indicates the importance of Mary, Joseph, and the shepherds in this event. The number and size of the angels are two examples of the many and often complex visual allusions included in this Nativity.

Perhaps less obvious is the significance of the angels' vesture. All are garbed as assisting ministers for a festive Mass, the celebration of Christ's death and resurrection. One wears a red and gold cope with the Latin word for "holy" repeated on its border, a reference to the chant sung at the climax of the Mass, as well as to the holy ground the angels are on—also indicated by Joseph's cast-off sandal.

Alfred Delp, the German Jesuit priest martyred by the Nazis, left this observation about the Christmas angels: "They announce God's mystery and summon the listeners to the adoration from which they themselves have risen. Their mystery is that they represent the afterglow of the divine reality they proclaim." Like the angels themselves, these three masterpieces capture in exquisite detail an afterglow of the Christmas events and point us to the divine mystery of love which the heavenly messengers proclaimed. ◈

SOURCE CITED

Delp, Alfred, *The Prison Meditations of Father Delp*, New York: The MacMillan Company, 1966

A former college instructor, travel agency coordinator, and pastor, free-lance art historian Phillip Gugel lives in St. Paul, Minnesota, where he researches, speaks, and writes about sacred art. This is his sixteenth consecutive article for *Christmas*.

Nativity from the *Portinari Altarpiece* 1474-1476.

Scala/Art Resource, NY 1.50041498 K37031 Color Transp. Goes, Hugo van der. Portinari Altarpiece—open, full view. Uffizi, Florence, Italy.

DECK THE HALLS
WITH CHRISTMAS ANGELS

REBECCA Jon MICHAELS

What could be a better symbol for Christmas than angels? And what could make more festive Yuletide decorations than beautiful hand-crafted Christmas angels?

Here are three lovely ornaments that will add a heavenly touch to your Christmas trimmings and provide delightful do-it-yourself activities for you or your entire family.

CUT-PAPER ANGELS

In the tradition of scherenschnitte—*German cut-paper art—these angel silhouettes can be framed against a colorful background or extended to make a whole chain of beautiful angels. The finished angels are 6½ x 6 inches.*

MATERIALS

- medium-weight white paper
- tracing paper
- pencil
- spoon
- paper scissors
- 8 x 10-inch picture frame
- colorful Christmas wrapping paper or dark mat board
- rubber cement

INSTRUCTIONS

1. Trace the pattern at right onto tracing paper. Note: If you are making a paper chain, trace only to the dotted line, leaving off the tips of angel's wing, robe, and foot (these sections will form links to the next angel in the chain).

2. Using a soft pencil, draw over the pattern lines on the reverse side of the tracing paper. Fold the white paper in half. Lay the pattern over the folded paper, lining up the broken lines on star and robe with the fold. Rub over the lines with the back of a spoon to transfer the pattern.

3. Cut out the shapes, beginning in the center of the design (at the fold) and working toward the outside. Hold the paper together firmly while cutting. Open out the paper.

4. Cut colorful Christmas wrapping paper or mat board to fit the picture frame. Glue the pair of angels in the center of the mat with several dots of rubber cement.

IDEAS AND OPTIONS

- If you want lots of angels, use the pattern to make a sturdy template from plastic or cardboard.

- To make a chain of angels, accordion-fold a strip of lightweight paper into 3-inch-wide folds. (A roll of shelf paper will make two long chains.) Tip: The more accurate your folds are, the better your angel chain will be. Transfer the pattern onto an end fold, lining up the broken lines with the paper edge and the dotted lines (at wing, robe, foot) with the fold. Holding the folds firmly together, carefully cut out pattern through all layers of paper. Be sure not to cut through joints at the folds. Cut several chains and tape matching ends together to make it longer.
- Tape an angel chain around a gift package for decoration.
- Tuck a chain of angels into greens on a mantle or over a doorway.

HANKY ANGEL

Got a handkerchief that's too pretty or too special to use? Here's a unique way to display its beauty: turn the hanky into an angel! This ornament is both quick and easy—an ideal project to do with young children. The finished angel looks lovely on the tree, in a wreath, or in a window.

MATERIALS

- 9-inch-square handkerchief
- 1½-inch diameter brass ring⋆
- 3 ribbon roses⋆
- Stapler or needle and thread
- Plastic canvas⋆
- Utility scissors
- Thick craft glue
- Gold cord to hang⋆

(⋆ available at craft or fabric stores)

INSTRUCTIONS

1. Use the pattern in diagram A on this page to cut two matching triangles from plastic canvas. Set these aside. Press the hanky, removing any creases. Fold the hanky in half on the diagonal. Refer to diagrams B and C to form wings, folding top corners down and then back. Centers of wings will overlap at back of angel; outside edges of wings should be parallel (see diagram D).

2. Insert the plastic canvas triangles into the wings, overlapping points of the triangles in the center. Staple through all thicknesses to secure wings in place. Or secure by stitching through all thicknesses with matching thread.

3. Place the ring slightly above the center section of angel so that its bottom lays over the top edge of the cloth. (See diagram E). Fold the cloth edge down over the loop to make a "collar" that covers the bottom of the ring. Staple or stitch in place. Glue ribbon roses over all staples.

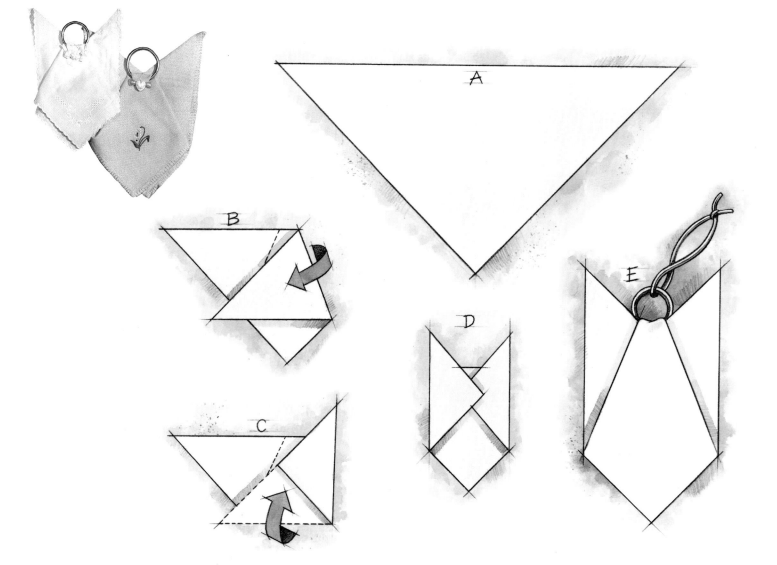

4. To hang the angel, knot together the ends of a thin 11-inch gold cord to form a loop. Put the midpoint of the loop through the ring, thread the knotted end through the loop, and pull tight to form a slip knot.

IDEAS AND OPTIONS:

- Use tiny dried roses or silk flowers instead of ribbon roses to decorate the angel.
- Use damask table napkins for larger angels. Adjust the size of the plastic canvas triangles to fit the larger wing size. Use a larger ring.
- For a country look, use 10-inch squares of homespun fabric. Fray the outer ½ inch on each side to finish the edges. Use small grapevine wreaths for halos.
- Stencil a border on inexpensive cloth napkins before folding them into the angel shape.

MUSLIN ANGEL

The simple beauty of this project is a reminder that wonderful things often result from humble origins. Perhaps you have a scrap of muslin just waiting to be transformed into this stunning angel. As a wall hanging, table-top ornament, or even a tree decoration, this 17-inch angel will delight the whole family.

MATERIALS

- 1 yard of 45-inch-wide unbleached muslin
- Sewing thread of matching color
- Tracing paper for pattern
- 36 x 18-inch piece of thin batting
- Pencil
- Masking tape
- Fabric scissors
- Small white plastic ring or ⅝ yard of white ribbon to hang

INSTRUCTIONS

1. Enlarge the patterns on page 54 onto tracing paper, making each square on the grid equal to one inch. From muslin, cut out two 20 x 18-inch pieces for the body and two 14 x 16-inch pieces for the wings. Tape the body pattern to a window or a light box. Tape one 20 x 18-inch piece of muslin over the pattern. Using a sharp pencil, trace the pattern lines onto the muslin. *Note: Do not trace the dotted lines; they are for wing placement after all stitching is completed.* In the same manner, transfer the pattern lines of the wings to one 14 x 16-inch piece of muslin.

2. Cut batting to fit the rectangles. Pin batting to the wrong side of each piece. Stitch the outline of each shape, sewing just outside the pattern lines. Pin each piece to the matching, unmarked piece of muslin, with right sides facing. Stitch the layers together, sewing just inside the stitched line. Leave an opening for turning where indicated on the pattern. Reinforce the underarm curves by stitching over the lines a second time.

3. Trim the excess fabric away from each piece, cutting ¼ inch outside the stitched line. Clip the curves to the seam line. Turn right side out and press. Slip-stitch the openings closed.

4. Machine or hand-stitch the detail lines on the angel and wings, except for the neck and bodice lines. When stitching is completed, lay the angel on top of the wings, referring to pattern's dotted lines for placement. Stitch through all layers along the neck, shoulders, and bodice lines to secure the wings to the angel's back.

5. Tack a small white plastic ring to the back side of the angel's head to hang. If you wish to hang your angel at the tree top, tack the midpoint of a ribbon to the angel's back. Tie the ribbon ends into a bow around the topmost branch to secure the angel.

IDEAS AND OPTIONS

- For a "country" angel, add a grapevine wreath for a halo, a corsage of dried flowers, and trailing ribbons.
- Shade the cheeks with powdered blush, using a cotton swab.
- Stitch the design lines of body and wings with colored thread if you want lines to be more pronounced.
- Use fabric paints to color the muslin after transferring the pattern outline. (When paint is dry, continue with step 2.)
- Use dimensional paint writers to decorate the angel.
- Cut decorations from sheets of glitter that can be fused in place with an iron. (Craft stores have a wide array of colors.) Follow the manufacturer's directions to fuse.
- Using a fabric other than muslin will give the angel a different look. White bridal satin will make a very elegant angel. You could add decorations of lace and ribbon. For a more colorful angel, use printed cottons. The face could be appliqued on a solid fabric.

Rebecca JonMichaels is a writer and crafts editor living in St. Charles, Illinois. When not designing angels, her passion in life is piecing quilts.

Photography by Leo Kim, Minneapolis, Minnesota.
Technical illustrations by RKB Studios, Minneapolis, Minnesota.

LEAVE OPEN

LEAVE OPEN

A VIOLIN
FOR MISS PEGGY

JONATHAN DONLEY

Ol' Rufe just seemed to materialize at the edge of town one day in July, stepping out of the heat waves shimmering above the corn. The scarecrow figure shuffled into Glenborough, head hunched low and intense, tattered brogans scuffling up clouds of dust. Despite the sweltering sun, I felt a little chill as he passed. Bess Kramer's dog, Peabucket, rolled off the porch and loped toward the lanky stranger, tail wagging and tongue lolling out of the side of his mouth. He nuzzled one of the man's hands in greeting.

Quick as a snake, the stranger spun and landed a vicious kick into Peabucket's belly. The poor dog whoofed as he slammed against the house, collapsing in a stunned heap.

I was so mad I couldn't make my mouth work right. I just shrieked. I got to Peabucket in time to see a smirk playing around one corner of the man's mouth. He looked up and locked his dead blue eyes on me. I froze, as still as if I'd seen a rattler coiled at my feet, cocked back and ready to strike.

"Boy," he hissed, "your dog tries to bite me again, I'm gonna stomp him dead." Then he wheeled and disappeared down the road. I stroked Peabucket's head and cried until Miz Kramer got home. She was mad as all git-out, but Rufe was long gone.

I hoped I'd seen the last of the stranger, but it wasn't to be. Rufe had bought the old Jenkins cabin, back in the woods along Kiowa Creek, and he settled in to stay. It didn't take long until he became the town character: the one kids snicker at, the one grownups pretend not to see, the one mommas use to threaten naughty kids.

The town dogs learned to give Rufe a wide berth over the next couple of years, and we kids mostly did the same.

Me and my little sister Ruthie would fall quiet and stare through the fence slats as he trudged into town, mutterin' at us through the salt-and-pepper whiskers he grew 'cause he was too cheap to buy a razor. He had a set of false teeth, but he rarely wore them. "Saves on wear and tear," he'd say. About once a week he ambled past the schoolhouse and across the square to Gramp Franklin's store. He'd sell some furs and buy bacon, flour, and other victuals, then make his way home, scowling all the while.

Some said Rufe was born mean; others said he was a man livin' with a hurt. Nobody knew for sure, and Rufe wasn't talking. Whatever had soured him on life, though, had worked on him until he didn't seem to have much use for the rest of humanity.

Bein' kids, I guess we would've made life a lot rougher for Rufe, if it hadn't been for Miss Peggy. Our schoolmistress was as sweet as Rufe was mean, an Irish lass whose red hair was showing frost and whose face had crinkled pleasantly over the half-century of prairie winters. She'd seen some years, but she was young inside and showed it.

She caught me once, shuffling down the aisle between wooden desks, slouched over in a parody of Ol' Rufe. I stopped in mid scowl to see those pretty hazel eyes fixed on me, eyebrows arched with disapproval. It was her "special" look, the kind that made you want to hide from her and fall in love with her all in the same breath.

"Matthew Colin O'Brien," she shook her head sadly. "It's a better man you'll grow to be if you care for your own faults, rather than those of others."

I could've crawled in a hole. I'd have sooner kissed Peabucket than disappoint Miss Peggy. I spent the rest of the day feelin' kinda sick because I thought she didn't like me anymore. But she gave me a little hug as I left the schoolhouse, and I knew the world was still a good place.

Her sweetness didn't stay at the schoolhouse. When anyone was sick, Miss Peggy would be there in the evenings, spinning magical tales of faraway or murmuring comfort from the Psalms. She even helped Ol' Rufe when he was laid up with fever, fixing his meals and brewing tea from willow bark and coneflower. He never showed any gratitude, of course, but that didn't seem to make any difference to Miss Peggy. She was a real lady.

The contrast between the two of them was never so plain as the night she asked him a favor at a town dance in early December. One of the few diversions we had was a social down at the church, with all the pews pulled against the walls to make way for dancers. Now this might sound strange to you, but Parson Lewis always said God invented fun, and doesn't mind a little good-spirited socializin' in his house. Anyway, it was the only building in town with enough room.

For all his meanness, Rufe could make a fiddle sing when he wanted, playing "Billy Bright" and "Round the Mountain" lively enough to pull you to your feet and set you dancing. And when he slid softly into "Bard of Armagh" or "Derry Air," it could draw tears from the toughest man there. Rufe didn't play for fun, of course, but for the nickels we collected. And though this added a sour note to the evening, we tolerated it for his music.

Rufe was tightening his bow that evening when Miss Peggy approached him.

"Your music is delightful, Rufus," she said. "How fortunate we are to have such a talented musician as our neighbor. You add such joy to these dances."

"I'm gettin' paid," Rufe shrugged.

Miss Peggy breezed past the gruffness.

"In a couple of weeks, sir, it's going to be Christmas. I'm working with the pupils on a Nativity play. I'll play piano, of course, but it would be lovelier with a violin."

A smile crinkled the corners of her eyes, and you could tell her heart was on something long ago.

"I remember when I was a child how the violins made the old carols sound so sweet," she said. "You could bring much happiness to the children if you would play, too. Would you share your music with us? Please?"

"Don't care much for kids," Rufe scowled. A hard smile touched his lips. "How much would you pay?"

Miss Peggy arched her eyebrows and gave Rufe her "special" look. He didn't appear to notice. She shook her head in what appeared to be pity and walked away.

Ol' Rufe just shrugged and picked up his fiddle.

I ran and hugged Miss Peggy; I couldn't stand to see her disappointed.

"How could anybody be so mean?" I asked.

She bent down until her frosty red curls filled my whole world and whispered: "Oh, Matthew, you need to learn to look deeper. Music doesn't lie. A man can't make music like that unless the True Song is playing somewhere inside him."

I wasn't sure what she meant by that—it took quite a few years before I knew for sure—but it had the ring of truth; and, if she believed it, I wanted to.

The days dragged and excitement mounted as Christmas approached. Now in those days, you couldn't just drive down to some superstore and buy Christmas Spirit all prepackaged and factory-fresh. What we had came from our hearts and hands, using love and creativity to make the season come alive. Homemade wreaths appeared on doors and in windows, and hand-dipped candles flickered in the hands of carved wooden angels. Gramp's store laid in an extra stock of baking goods, and candy canes appeared in his front window.

Fathers worked by lamplight making wooden toys, and mothers stitched rag dolls and corncob dolls and baked wondrous things steaming with ginger and cinnamon. It was a time made for kids, and we made the most of it.

One morning, the week before Christmas, Miss Peggy didn't ring the school bell. We found her in her little house behind the school, shivering and burning with fever—the kind that often led to death in those days.

We got an early vacation for Christmas that year, but we didn't like it. It was too cold to play outside much, and we weren't really in the mood for play. Mostly we hung around Miss Peggy's little house, running errands for whoever was nursing her, and waiting for word from the doctor.

Even the grownups seemed to find business taking them by Miss Peggy's a bit more than usual. It seemed there was always a little group clustered on the front porch, or leaning against the picket fence. Every once in a while, during an errand, I'd get to see Miss Peggy. She just lay there, quiet and pale, with a quilt pulled around her chin, for once looking her age. A glance at her sent me running out in the snow. Imagine the world without Miss Peggy! The tears just came and came.

The whole town was holding its breath, waiting to see if Miss Peggy would live or die. The whole town except Ol' Rufe, of course. He shuffled into town Christmas Eve morning, his brogans leaving long marks in the snow. He glanced at the group huddled on Miss Peggy's front porch, muttered something about "malingerers," and trudged a little faster toward Gramp's store.

A little while later, Doc Perkins came to check on Miss Peggy. When he came out, he was pale and white-lipped;

he just shook his head. When Doc told us in his gentle way that Miss Peggy probably wouldn't last the night, all the magic just sort of melted out of Christmas.

Looking back, I'm ashamed of the way I felt, even though it was out of love for Miss Peggy. But Ruthie was speaking for me, too, when she blurted out her feelings in the kind of honesty only a hurt child can express.

"Oh, Matt!" she wailed in a voice clear enough for half the town to hear. "Why does God have to take Miss Peggy away? Why can't Ol' Rufe die instead?" I might've answered her—and I guess the same thought was running through my head—but when I looked up, Rufe was standing on the street, a box of food under one arm. I mentally ducked for an outburst; but instead of yelling, Rufe just stared at Ruthie with a sort of stunned expression, like maybe she'd stuck him with a knife. It was the same stunned look that I'd seen on Peabucket's face the first day Rufe kicked him. Then Rufe stirred and walked quickly past the schoolhouse without a word.

None of us felt like putting on the Christmas play that night, but it seemed like the thing to do. Miss Peggy had put so much into it— writing it up, practicing the songs, helping us get our parts right—before she took sick. We knew she would want us to have the play, even if she couldn't be there with us.

Momma gave me and Ruthie a hug before we left for the church and told us that Christmas—and the real thing behind it—would always go on, no matter what happened to Miss Peggy.

"She'd want it that way," Momma said. "And she'd want you to do your very best tonight."

Closing my eyes against the tears, I could see Miss Peggy nodding.

Most of the town gathered for the Christmas program that night, but it seemed more like a funeral service than a celebration. Mary and Joseph had tear-swollen eyes, the wise men looked at the ground instead of the star, and even baby Jesus' halo seemed to droop.

Nobody wanted to leave afterward, so the parson suggested we wait awhile and pray for Miss Peggy. That was

fine with us. Sometimes, the only thing you can do when you're hurting is just to hold onto one another. We knelt by our pews and began to pray.

Sometime later, the parson said "Amen," and we sat up quietly and held our own troubled thoughts.

I don't know how long it took for the music to penetrate my tears, but suddenly I became aware of a violin playing strains of "Silent Night."

With a curious murmur, the congregation stood and jostled in the aisle, then rushed out the church door and through the street toward the music.

We rumbled to a halt in front of Miss Peggy's house. There stood Ol' Rufe, fiddle under his chin, playing the old carol like it was from the heart. The moon was nearly full, and in the harsh light, we could see tears streaming from his tightly closed eyes and shimmering on his cheeks.

Everyone's heard "Silent Night," but—oh!—never like it sounded that night in Glenborough. We stood mute for two whole verses, looking for the world like silver statues in the moonlit snow. Across the sky, stars leaped from the blackness as they can on only the bitterest of winter nights. In the woods, a whippoorwill chimed in to accompany the lone violin.

Then we started singing. There, under the glowing heavens, it seemed as if a flock of white-robed angels had landed on Miss Peggy's front yard to sing praises. Now maybe you've never felt the toasty chillbumps that come on Christmas Eve—the thrill that comes when stars hang brilliant in blackness and your family sits cozy before a flickering fire and breathes air heavy with evergreen and sings carols that turn time back two thousand years. If you've never felt it, I'm sorry for you. That night we sang the True Song—we climbed right inside it, if you know what I mean. And those warm chillbumps just came and came and wouldn't go away.

Once we got warmed up to the spirit of things, we sang one carol after another, from "Adeste Fideles" to "Away in the Manger." And as he played along with us, we watched the meanness just sort of fall off Ol' Rufe like a dirty shirt. It seemed that the sour old hermit had died, just like Ruthie wished, and another Rufe had come to take his place.

When we'd sung every verse of every carol we knew and hummed through about five more, we all kind of grew quiet and peaceful. And in the magical spell our carols had woven, we stood staring at Miss Peggy's house.

A splash of light broke the magic as Doc Perkins stepped through the front door. We caught our breath, waiting for the worst. But Doc gave us a haggard smile and said: "The fever's broken. She's going to make it."

As tired as we were, we went wild, hugging each other and laughing with relief. Then, after he'd quieted us down, the parson led us in a prayer of thanks.

I wondered, as we straggled home before dawn, whether it was the prayers or the music—or something else altogether—that made the difference between Miss Peggy's living or dying. You're going to have to decide for yourself. But if you put it all down to coincidence, it's your loss. For myself, I never quit wondering until I learned the True Song by heart.

We got two presents that Christmas: our Miss Peggy back again and a new Rufe. And there was a third present, although that came a little later. You see, Rufe took to wearing his teeth, bought himself a razor, and began to walk taller. Then he started to drop in on Miss Peggy. And, although we'll always call her "Miss Peggy," by the next Christmas, our beloved teacher was busy turning the old Jenkins place into a respectable home for newlyweds.

Jonathan Donley is an editor for a daily newspaper in San Antonio, Texas. His story was inspired by his mother's tales of pioneer Texas ancestors, his grandmother's songs, his father's sermons and his own barefoot childhood. He says the "True Song" happens every Christmas Eve when he and his children gather under the deep, still heavens to play guitar, sing carols and watch angels glide down on moonbeams to renew the joyful message of hope.

Illustrations by Rosanne Kaloustian, Bayside, New York. Since 1983 Rosanne has illustrated numerous books for children and her work has won several awards.

THE SMALL STIRRING

*S*e e at this most holy hour
  The radiance of the star:
    Glancing, slanting
        shards of light
    Prisming into clarity
        the act,
      the epiphany,
      the moment.

*K*n o w at this most holy hour
  The yearning of the women:
    Elizabeth longing,
        Mary pondering,
          Rachel weeping,
    Bearing each the knowing,
        the mystery,
        the cost.

*F*e e l at this most holy hour
  The rousing of the shepherds:
    Sleeping souls jostled,
        shaken
        startled
            into dread
            and grief
            and glory.

*A*w a i t at this most holy hour
  The coming of the Wonder:
    Centuries of silence
        broken by
    the small stirring,
        the gentle quickening,
        the Bright New Life.

JUNE BARROW

June Barrow is a college administrator, wife and mother of two children. She has taught English in high schools and colleges, and is currently active in a children's ministry to her church and community. Her home is in Greenwood, Indiana.

Illustration by Craig Claeys, Richfield, Minnesota. Border illustration by Dan Reed.

HEAVENLY CHRISTMAS TREATS

CINDY SYME

ere are recipes for four Christmas treats that will delight your palate and add a festive flair to your holiday table. The recipe for stained glass angel cookies also explains how to transform the cookies into dazzling ornaments for your tree or window.

For elegant gifts that say "made especially for you," pack an assortment of the cookies in a fancy tin, or wrap the cake with colorful foil and add a Christmas bow.

CARAMEL PRALINE ANGEL COFFEECAKE

3-3½ cups flour
¼ cup sugar
1 teaspoon salt
1 package dry yeast
¼ cup butter
¾ cup milk
2 eggs
Filling
Glaze
2 tablespoons sliced almonds
1 tablespoon raisins or dried cranberries

1. In large mixing bowl, combine 1 cup flour, sugar, salt and yeast.
2. In medium saucepan, melt butter and add milk. Heat until very warm (125°-130°).
3. Stir into dry ingredients. Beat in eggs. Add enough of the remaining flour to form a soft dough.
4. On floured surface, knead dough for 5 minutes. Form into ball, and place in greased bowl, turning once to grease top of dough. Cover with towel and allow to rise in a warm place for 1 hour or until doubled in size.
5. To create body and head of angel, divide dough in half. Roll out one half on lightly floured surface to a 10" x 10" square. Spread half of filling to within 1" of edges. Fold in half, pinching edges tightly and tucking seams

under. Place dough on lightly greased baking sheet. Twist top third of rectangle to create head. Round edges of head with fingers.

6. To create wings, roll out other half of dough into a 10" circle. Cut in half. Spread each half with filling to within 1" of edges. Fold in half to make a quarter circle, pinching edges firmly together and tucking seams under. Place each quarter circle slightly under dough on either side of body to form wings.

7. With sharp knife, cut partially through dough around head to outline a halo. Decorate halo with sliced almonds, and use raisins or dried cranberries for face.

8. Cover and allow to rise 30-40 minutes.

9. Heat oven to 350°. Bake 20-25 minutes until lightly browned. Carefully remove to wire cooling rack using two spatulas. Allow to cool.

10. Drizzle body and wings with almond glaze.

Filling:
½ cup brown sugar
½ cup butter
1 teaspoon vanilla
½ cup toasted slivered almonds (to toast: place in 350° oven for 5-7 minutes)
1 egg

1. In medium bowl, beat together brown sugar and butter.
2. Mix in remaining ingredients.

Almond Glaze:
¾ cup powdered sugar
3 teaspoons milk
½ teaspoon almond extract

Whisk together ingredients and keep covered until used.

PEPPERMINT SUGAR COOKIES

Makes 2-3 dozen, depending on size of cookie cutters

⅓ cup butter, softened
⅓ cup shortening
¾ cup sugar
1 egg
½ teaspoon peppermint extract
4 drops red food coloring
1½ teaspoons baking powder
½ teaspoon salt
2 cups flour
Sparkling and colored sugars

1. In large mixing bowl, cream butter, shortening, and sugar until light and fluffy. Add egg and beat well.

2. Stir in peppermint extract, baking powder, and salt. Mix until combined.

3. Gradually add flour and mix just until combined.

4. Chill overnight in refrigerator.

5. Heat oven to 375°. Roll out one half of dough on floured surface to ⅛" thickness. Using cookie cutters in heavenly shapes, cut dough into angels, harps, trumpets, drums and clouds.

6. Place cut dough on cookie sheets at least 2" apart. Sprinkle with sparkling or colored sugars.

7. Bake 6-8 minutes until firm but still light in color. Remove from cookie sheet and cool on wire rack.

STAINED GLASS ANGEL COOKIES

Makes 2-3 dozen, depending on size of angels

½ cup butter, softened
¾ cup sugar
¼ cup sour cream
1 egg
1 teaspoon vanilla
½ teaspoon rum extract (optional)
1½ teaspoons baking powder
½ teaspoon baking soda
½ teaspoon salt
2 cups flour
Assorted colored hard candies
Decorative frostings

1. In large bowl, cream butter and sugar until light and fluffy. Mix in sour cream, egg, vanilla, and rum extract (if using). Add baking powder, soda, and salt.

2. Gradually add flour and mix until just combined.

3. Refrigerate dough several hours or overnight.

4. Heat oven to 350°. Divide dough in half and roll out one half at a time on floured surface to ⅛" thickness. Using angel-shaped cookie cutters that are at least 3" high, cut dough and place on aluminum-foil-lined cookie sheets 1½" apart.

5. On the body or wings of angels, cut out a design using small aspic cutters or a very sharp knife.
To make this step easier, chill dough on cookie sheets for 10-15 minutes in refrigerator before cutting detailed stained glass designs.

6. Separate the hard candy colors, and place in zipper-lock plastic bags. Crush candies into small pieces using a hammer.

7. Carefully fill each small stained glass hole with crushed hard candies of the same color. Try to keep the crushed candy within the cut area and fill as full as possible.

8. Bake cookies 7-10 minutes until candies are melted, and the cookies are firm but not browned. Remove from oven and allow cookies to cool in pan for a minute to make sure candy sets. Remove and cool completely on wire rack. Add decorative frosting for a face or other angelic details.
These cookies can make dazzling Christmas ornaments. Prior to baking, use a drinking straw to punch a small hole at the top of the angel. After baked cookies have cooled, thread yarn or ribbon through the hole for hanging on your tree or in a window.

ORANGE CARDAMOM ANGEL WINGS

Makes 4 dozen

1 cup butter, softened
⅔ cup sugar
2 tablespoons grated orange peel
1 teaspoon cardamom
¼ teaspoon salt
2 cups flour
Coarse-grained white sparkling sugar
Gold or silver decors, or other decorating candy

1. Heat oven to 350°.

2. In large bowl, cream butter and sugar. Add orange peel, cardamom, and salt. Add flour and mix well.

3. To shape wings: for each pair of wings, divide 1 tablespoon of dough in half. Roll each half into a 7" rope and place side by side on an ungreased baking sheet. Coil each rope into a spiral (left wing, clockwise; right wing, counterclockwise), leaving 1" at top of coils to add angel's head to baking sheet.

4. To shape head and halo: Divide one teaspoon of dough in half. Shape half of dough into ball and gently press onto top of wings to form head. Roll remaining half into a 2" rope halo. Lay halo around angel's head, pressing very gently to adhere. Arrange gold or silver decors to form eyes and to decorate halo. Sprinkle with sparkling sugar.

5. Bake for 7-9 minutes or until golden brown. Cool on wire rack.

Cindy Syme is a free-lance food stylist and consultant in the twin cities of St. Paul and Minneapolis. No matter how busy she is at Christmas, Cindy always makes time to "share good things from the oven."

Photograpy by Leo Kim, Minneapolis, Minnesota.

CHRISTMAS MEMORIES

CHRISTMAS EVE

_____

_____

_____

_____

CHRISTMAS DAY

_____

_____

_____

MENU

_____

_____

WORSHIP SERVICES

_____

_____

_____

GIFTS   FROM

_____   _____

_____   _____

_____   _____

_____   _____

GUESTS

_____ _____ _____

_____ _____ _____

_____ _____ _____

ACKNOWLEDGMENTS
Scripture text for "The Christmas Story" and "Invitation" is from _The Holy Bible, New King James Version_, copyright © 1979, 1980, 1982 Thomas Nelson, Inc. Used by permission. All other scripture references are from the New Revised Standard Version Bible, copyright © 1989 Division of Christian Education of the National Council of the Churches of Christ in the USA and used by permission. Prayers in "Worshiping with Angels" are reprinted from _Lutheran Book of Worship_, copyright © 1978. Text, tunes, and settings of "Oh, Come, Oh, Come, Emmanuel"; "Lo, How a Rose Is Growing"; and "The First Noel" are taken from _Lutheran Book of Worship_, copyright © 1978. Used by permission. "Invitation" text copyright © Sr. Mary Winifred, CHS. Used by permission. "Waiting for Jesus" text copyright © Harold Webb Eppley and Rochelle Yolanda Melander. Used by permission. "The Angels' Anthem" text copyright © Mary Lou Healy. Used by permission. "Worshiping with Angels" text copyright © David W. Toht. Used by permission. "Let the Stable Still Astonish" text copyright © Leslie Leyland Fields. Used by permission. "Children, Imagination, and Christmas Angels" text copyright © Bob Hartman. Used by permission. "The Gift" text copyright © Marilyn Koetz. Used by permission. "Looking Toward Christmas" text copyright © Caryl Porter. Used by permission. "Messengers of His Birth" text copyright © Phillip Gugel. Used by permission. "The Expectation of Angels" text copyright © Nola Garrett. Used by permission. "Deck the Halls with Christmas Angels" text copyright © Rebecca JonMichaels. Used by permission. "A Violin for Miss Peggy" text copyright © Jonathan Donley. Used by permission. "The Small Stirring" text copyright © June Barrow. Used by permission. "Heavenly Christmas Treats" text copyright © Cindy Syme. Used by permission. Border illustration on this page is by Dan Reed.